THEO..

edited by

Timothy Pain

Scripture Union
130 City Road, London EC1V 2NJ

© Timothy Pain 1993

First published 1993

ISBN 0 86201 842 0

British Library Cataloguing-in-Publication Data.
A catalogue record for this book is available from the British
Library.

Book design and illustration by Tony Cantale Graphics.
Cover by Ross Advertising Design Limited.

Phototypeset by Intype, London.
Printed and bound in Great Britain by Cox and Wyman Ltd,
Reading.

A note from the editor

Two years ago I was on holiday with my family in north-east Greece. Like most tourists we spent much of our time visiting archeological sites and inspecting ruins.

One day we were looking round a small museum when my seven-year-old twin boys became bored with examining yet more clay pots. They started fidgeting, began playing around, and – before I could stop them – they sent an ancient Greek urn crashing to the floor where it smashed into a thousand pieces.

It would have been an expensive disaster, but for the fact that the accident revealed a packet of sealed papers which had been hidden in the urn for centuries.

To cover my embarrassment I expressed some professional interest in the find. So, a few months later, the curator of the museum kindly sent me the experts' evaluation of the find. They were rather disappointed that the papers had only turned out to be the private correspondence of a local physician who had lived in the first century AD.

Most of the letters were rather dull, but among them were some from a colleague which were much more interesting. And it is these which have attracted so much attention in the media.

Last year I asked the curator to forward me a facsimile of the letters, and I have now translated the more interesting ones into contemporary English.

Throughout the letters, for the sake of clarity, I have substituted the nearest modern equivalents for those first–century terms which are meaningless to twentieth-century readers.

The only substantial alteration I have made is to the date. But I assure you that the date is as it would have been had they followed our calendar.

Timothy Pain

A
selection
of Luke's letters

to
His excellency
Theophilus Primarius
The Senior Public Physician
Philippi
The Province of
Macedonia

Dear Theophilus,

Extraordinary news!

Three days ago, just before the Jews celebrated their feast of Lamb and Unleavened Bread, two visitors called at my lodgings.

My landlady was so excited by their arrival that she sent a messenger to summon me from my dispensary. I recognised one of them immediately: he's the man who brought me to Philippi.

It was eight years since I last saw him, and he'd come all the way from Ephesus to find me – and to offer me the temporary position of private physician to a group of travellers who are making the dangerous sea journey to Jerusalem.

Doubtless you'll think me irresponsible to leave my patients for a full quarter of the year. But you know how much I've always wanted to visit Jerusalem; and don't forget you've always said that you'd care for my patients if I had to be away. I'm taking you at your word!

I've left a detailed list at my dispensary of the medications and infusions I'm using with each patient. But don't feel obliged to follow them if you know better remedies. Do what you think best. I won't blame you if some of them die!

We sail on tonight's tide for Troas. I'll send you a full explanation from there.

Your loving friend,

Luke

Dear Theophilus,

Yesterday afternoon I was sitting on deck in the sunshine, hoping that you hadn't minded tending my patients for a few months, when I realised that I'd never explained to you how I first came to Philippi. If you don't know that, you'll never understand why I dropped everything to leave with my two visitors.

Eight years ago, I'd just completed my apprenticeship as herbalist and physician, and was living across the Aegean Sea here in Troas. Work was hard to come by, and I had to accept everything that came my way.

One day a stranger came to my room asking for a poultice to ease his master's troublesome eyes. My prescription must have brought some relief, for a few days later he returned and asked me to accompany them on the sea crossing from Troas to Philippi. You know how rough that crossing can be, and as his master has an aversion to sea travel, he wanted a physician at hand the whole time.

Well, the stranger was called Timothy, and his master was a small Jew with a squint and continually discharging eyes called Paul. Even though he spoke with a slight stammer, I soon discovered that Paul was a considerable scholar and a great debater. But you can imagine how embarrassed I was when I found that I'd accepted employment from a religious fanatic.

Paul was the first follower of the Jew Jesus that I'd come across, and he was one of the new movement's most energetic leaders. When we arrived in Philippi he immediately began lecturing the people at the Water Gate, and I was amazed when several accepted what he said.

I thought that Paul was talking nonsense then, and eight years later I still don't understand how anyone as educated as he can believe that a dead man returned to life.

Anyway, Timothy asked me to cleanse Paul's eyes for as

long as they stayed in Philippi. But after a few days an incident took place which ended with the two men vanishing from my life until last week.

You must remember the small earthquake which destroyed the town jail. Paul and one of his companions were locked in the jail when it happened – I think that I would have been inside too if I'd been a member of their sect!

Paul's public debating had caused a riot (they seem to happen everywhere he goes, which is partly why he needs a travelling physician) and the town magistrates had had him stripped, flogged, and thrown in prison.

All the prison doors burst open when the earthquake occurred. But instead of escaping, Paul persuaded all the prisoners to stay in their places.

I went to the prison at daylight, and was busy anointing Paul's wounds when the magistrates arrived in a panic. They'd just discovered that Paul possessed Roman citizenship and were terrified at the consequences of beating him. They begged him to leave Philippi. Which he did. He gave me my pay, my fare back to Troas, a generous bonus, and immediately left for Amphipolis. However, there were so many people who needed a physician in the weeks after the earthquake that I stayed on in Philippi – for eight years!

During those years, Theo, you have been kind enough to befriend me and to extend my knowledge of herbs and healing, but I've never mentioned my slight contact with the Way (that's what the followers of Jesus call themselves today).

My landlady is one of Paul's disciples, and from time to time she's talked to me about the Way. I've never been convinced by what she's said, but her Jesus must have been an exceptional person to have started such a fast-growing sect.

Anyway, all of this is only to explain what a surprise it was last week to see Timothy again, and to explain the excitement I felt when he said that Paul had sent him 350 miles to find me, and to persuade me to accompany them on another sea journey – this time right across the Aegean and the Mediterranean to Jerusalem.

At first I was reluctant to leave my patients, but somehow I felt compelled to go. Timothy said that we had to leave Philippi immediately because Paul wanted to reach Jersualem in time for the feast of First Fruits (you know what the Jews are like about their festivals). So we walked the eight miles to Neapolis and boarded the first boat for Troas.

The weather has been kind to us, and the sea crossing to Troas only took five days. Paul is due here tomorrow, and we'll be staying a few days while the party assembles.

I'm going to visit some friends from my time here as an apprentice; maybe I'll tell them a few of your ideas about healing – and pretend that they're my own invention!

I'll send you another note from the next port.

Your loving friend,

Luke.

6th May AD58   **Miletus**
                                                               West Asia

Dear Theophilus,

We stayed in Troas for a whole week while Paul's colleagues arrived from the surrounding area. There are ten of us in all, but I feel a little left out as I'm the only one who isn't part of the Way. I'm also the only qualified physician, yet something happened on the last day at Troas which shook my mind like a sieve in a young woman's hands.

If I relate the details in this letter you will be convinced that I've lost my ability to make an accurate diagnosis. So remind me, when I'm back in Philippi, to describe what happened to Eutychus. I still don't know how I made such a serious error of diagnosis.

From Troas we sailed south down the Asian coast calling at Assos, Mitylene, Chios, Samos and Trogyllium, before stopping here at Miletus for a few days. (I've included a sketch

DALMATIA
MOESIA SUPERIOR
MACEDONIA
Thessalonica
Philippi
Neapolis
Amphipolis
THRACE
AEGEAN SEA
Mytilene
Troas
Assos
Chios
Samos
Smyrna
ASIA
Ephesus
Miletus
Cos
Cridus
Rhodes
LYCIA
Patara
GALATIA
MEDITERRANEAN SEA
CILICIA
CYPRUS
PHOENICIA
Tyre
Caesaria Maritima
Ptolemais
SYRIA
PALAESTINA
Jerusalem
ARABIA

in case your geography isn't as good as your herbalism.) Paul so dislikes sea travel that he insisted on walking from Troas to Assos while we sailed!

At the moment the others are waiting for the leaders of Paul's disciples in Ephesus to come out and meet them. Apparently Paul caused a riot there three months ago and thinks it's too dangerous for him to visit the city in person. I gather that this riot has convinced Paul he's going to face even more violence in the future. So I might soon be busier than I have been thus far.

Please greet my landlady Lydia (she runs the purple-dye business near the Water Gate) and tell her that I am well. Use any of my herbs, ointments and potions that are still fresh, and tell all my patients that I should be back in Philippi by the beginning of August.

Your loving friend,

Luke,

19th May AD58

Tyre
Phoenicia

Dear Theophilus,

The disciples I told you about did eventually arrive from Ephesus, and I found out from one of them just how serious the riot had been.

Yet despite all the difficulties that Paul has brought upon them, they still seem to have a tremendous affection for him: most of them were in tears when he left.

The ten of us boarded a new boat at Miletus and sailed north of Rhodes to Patara. We changed ships there and found one which was heading for the province of Phoenicia. Then we sailed round the south of Cyprus to Tyre, and have been waiting here a week while the crew have unloaded the cargo.

Groups of disciples have come out to meet Paul wherever we have stopped, and they've all begged him not to go to Jerusalem.

He won't take any notice of them, but their requests and warnings have changed the mood of the party. There was much laughter on the boat to Miletus, but the closer we sail to Palaestina the more serious everyone becomes.

With best wishes,

Luke.

P.S. If Janus' stomach complaint hasn't cleared up, start prescribing a daily cake of dried figs.

Dear Theo,   24 May AD58.

Our sea voyages ended
when we landed rfirst at
Ptolemais, then at
Caesarea Maritima, its the capital
city of this province and possesses
an impressive fortress, an enormous
harbour, and the two biggest aqueducts
I've seen: one of them brings water
from a mountain six miles away!
However we've been told not to explore
because there's been terrible rioting
between the Jews and the Syrian settlers.
Our difficulties shouldn't be too
great because Timothy says there's hardly
enough time to reach Jerusalem
before First Fruits begins.

    Best wishes   LUKE.

Caesarea Maritima, Samaria, Palaestina

POST CARD

His
The S
Phi
Philip
Maed

13

Dear Theophilus,

Please excuse me for writing what's bound to be a very long letter: the last two weeks have been so exciting that I must describe them to somebody.

You'll see that I'm already back in the port of Caesarea Maritima, but instead of returning here quietly on foot with a few friends, I rode here on a horse escorted by two Roman centurions and two hundred armed soldiers!

Let me explain what has happened. When we arrived in Maritima we stayed with a man called Philip. He is one of Paul's colleagues and has been a leader among the followers of Jesus for even longer than Paul. Philip has four unmarried daughters, and I'm writing this letter from their house. They are delightful company and I won't mind how long I am forced to stay with them.

When we arrived there was the usual procession of disciples begging Paul not to visit Jerusalem. One of them even took Paul's belt and tied him up. But the man is so obstinate that we were soon walking south towards Jerusalem. Philip and some of the disciples from Maritima accompanied us as they wanted to escape from the riots and celebrate First Fruits in Jerusalem.

It's a two–day journey by foot and we stopped overnight in a small town called Antipatris, where we stayed with a Cypriot called Mnason. He's been a disciple for nearly thirty years, and is the first person I've met who knew Jesus personally.

When we arrived in Jerusalem we were taken to meet James: he's one of Jesus' brothers and seems to be the most senior leader of the Way. Paul handed him a very large sum of money which he'd collected from Asian and Macedonian disciples for famine relief in this province (I now think that this must have been the main purpose of our journey). And he gave James a detailed account of his work, boasting about how many of us non-Jews have become disciples.

It was a strange and tense meeting. I was a complete outsider. And Paul and James acted like two stray dogs sniffing around each other with their tails in the air.

James finally asked Paul to prove that he was still a good Jew by going to the Temple to make a vow and have his head shaved. Paul agreed, and went along with four others: he had to pay for their expensive sacrifices and haircuts as well as for his own!

At least this vow ensured that Paul was on his best behaviour and couldn't debate or preach, so I spent five peaceful days walking around Jerusalem talking with him and caring for his eyes. On the sixth day, Paul left me alone with my thoughts while he went off to pray in the Temple.

While he was there he was spotted by some Jews from Ephesus (I think I told you that he'd caused a riot there a few months ago) and they stirred up the crowd and seized him. They accused him of taking a non-Jew, Trophimus, into the part of the Temple that's restricted to Jews. (Trophimus is one of our party, and they must have recognised him because he comes from Ephesus.) Everybody believed them and the whole city was roused. People came running from all sides. Paul was dragged out of the Temple, and they set about trying to kill him.

I arrived with my ointments and bandages just as a Roman officer from the Antonia fortress (which overlooks the Temple area from the northwest corner) rescued Paul by charging on the crowd with his soldiers and centurions.

The Roman officer bound Paul with two chains and tried to take him into the fortress. But the crowd was so violent and noisy that Paul had to be carried overhead by the soldiers while the mob screamed for his death. You should have seen me pushing through the crowd with my bag, trying to reach Paul!

Instead of going quietly, Paul asked the soldiers to set him down at the top of the steps into the fortress so that he could speak to the crowd. I couldn't understand much of what he said because he spoke in Aramaic, but I gather that he started explaining how he'd changed from an enthusiastic opponent of Jesus' followers into a convinced advocate of their cause.

He hadn't been speaking for more than a few minutes when the crowd began waving their cloaks about, throwing dust in the air, and yelling so loudly that the soldiers bundled Paul into the fortress and locked the door. I was left outside on the steps and had to make my own way through the seething crowd to our lodgings – I've never been so frightened in my life.

Paul was freed the next day, and had to appear before the Jerusalem Council. It was a public hearing so I was able to be there. When Paul began speaking the High Priest ordered one of his attendants to strike Paul on the mouth. As I hadn't been able to cleanse his eyes that morning Paul didn't recognise who'd given the order, and he cursed the High Priest, calling him a whitewashed wall. It was not a good beginning to the hearing!

Paul then tried to identify himself with one of the two groups which make up the Council by talking about his favourite topic – the return from the dead. Everyone started shouting at the same time, and the Roman officer thought that Paul was going to be torn to pieces. So he sent his troops in to haul Paul out and take him back to the Antonia fortress.

Next day, one of Paul's nephews told me that he'd overheard forty Jews preparing an ambush for Paul and vowing not to eat or drink until they'd killed him. I went straight to the fortress with the nephew and told Paul about the plot. He called over one of the centurions who took the nephew to Claudius Lysias, the Senior Officer, and he decided on a dramatic midnight escape.

All of Paul's other companions had to stay behind. Only I was allowed to travel with him, as his private physician. We were given horses, and were escorted out of Jerusalem at nine in the evening by two centurions, two hundred soldiers, seventy cavalry and two hundred auxiliaries. We made Antipatris by daybreak, where the foot soldiers left us, and rode on quickly to Caesarea Maritima.

We were taken straight to the Governor's residence, and a soldier handed a note from Claudius Lysias to Antonius Felix, the Governor, which explained the situation. Felix ordered Paul to be held in his palace, and said that he would hear the case as soon as Paul's accusers arrived.

So here I am, staying with Philip's four daughters while their father is away in Jerusalem! I've been here three days now and am greatly enjoying the use of the horse I was given by Claudius Lysias. I visit Paul each morning to bathe his eyes and anoint his bruises; I spend the rest of the day with the youngest daughter, Julia, struggling to learn a little Aramaic and hearing a lot about the recent disturbances here and her devotion to the founder of her sect.

Paul's accusers are due in a few days and I'm sure that he will be released immediately. I doubt whether he'll return to Jerusalem, so I could soon be on a boat bound for Philippi. You must make sure that my patients are better by then!

Please visit Lydia and tell her all my news. Reassure her that Paul is safe and well, and so am I.

With best wishes,
Your loving friend,

Luke,

P.S. I hope that you remembered to make fresh infusions for Erastus and Andronica – the ones I left in my dispensary should have been discarded at the end of a month.

Dear Theophilus,

When I wrote to you a month ago I fully expected that Paul would be free by now and that I'd be sailing towards Philippi. But as you can see, I'm still stuck in Caesarea Maritima and growing more impatient with each day that passes.

The Jewish race must be the most hot-headed, inflexible and argumentative group of people that it's ever been my misfortune to meet. This ridiculous dispute would have been resolved immediately anywhere else in the Empire. It should have been settled here two weeks ago; yet it looks as though it will drag on for months.

Two days after my last letter to you the Jewish High Priest Ananias (that's the man Paul called a whitewashed wall) arrived together with some leading members of the Jerusalem Council and a lawyer named Tertullus. The trial was a mockery of imperial justice.

Tertullus opened for the prosecution with an eloquent speech which praised the Governor for his foresight, reforms, graciousness and peaceful six-year reign – when it's common knowledge that Antonius Felix is greedy, cruel and immoral, and that the Jews hate him as much as they hate all Romans.

Tertullus went on – rightly – to accuse Paul of being a perfect pest, of stirring up trouble among the Jews the world over, and of being a ringleader of the Jesus sect.

Now if Tertullus had stopped there I would have agreed with him. But he went on to charge Paul with profaning the Temple, and I know that Trophimus didn't set foot in the place.

Ananias and his colleagues all supported Tertullus, then Felix motioned Paul to speak. It must have been the first time that he has ever been able to deny arguing with anyone or stirring up a mob! Paul maintained that his opponents couldn't prove any of their accusations, and went on to argue that the Way was part of the Jewish religion. You should have seen Ananias' face when he heard Paul say this!

Paul explained to Felix that he had come on a pilgrimage to Jerusalem to bring a large sum of relief-money to his nation. I suspect that it is this which has caused all the delay, for now Felix is convinced that Paul is wealthy and keeps on postponing his judgement in the hope that Paul will offer him money. He doesn't know Paul.

Paul closed his speech with yet another sermon about people returning from the dead, at which Felix leapt to his feet and abruptly ended Paul's lecture by announcing that the trial was adjourned. He promised to give his judgement when the Senior Roman Officer in Jerusalem, Claudius Lysias, came to Maritima.

Paul is still under arrest in the fortress, and the best I can say about Antonius Felix is that he doesn't prevent me from attending to Paul's needs. Lysias has come and gone twice but Felix still refuses to give a decision. He's had several private conversations with Paul, and I think that Felix's wife Drusilla was present at one of them.

Of course Paul doesn't help himself. He told me that at his last meeting he lectured Felix about the importance of self-control, morality, and the final judgement!

He has offered to release me from his service, but I can't bring myself to leave him while he's under arrest. Julia is still helping me to understand a few words of Aramaic, but now that Philip has returned from Jerusalem I'm unable to spend as much time alone with her as I'd like.

All of the wounds from Paul's severe beating have healed, and it now takes me only a short time each morning to cleanse his eyes: the rest of each day is my own. Because of the problems here between the Jews and the Syrians, the authorities won't allow me to practise as a physician unless I agree to settle. So I'm using the time to become an expert on Caesarea Maritima and the Roman occupation of Palaestina.

I've also learnt a great deal about the history of the Way: thanks to Julia, I've twice been able to surprise Paul with a fact about Jesus that he didn't know!

Theo, my good friend, as your advice has always been so helpful in the past, I would appreciate some suggestions for the best use of my time while I am unable to work as a physician.

Please write back as soon as you can, and include news of all my patients and any new treatments you've tried on them.

Pass on my affectionate greetings to Lydia, and try to persuade her to put my effects into store and to let my room to someone else. Philip and his daughters join me in sending greetings to you.

With best wishes,
Your good friend,

Luke.

26th August AD58

Caesarea Maritima
Samaria
Palaestina

Dear Theophilus,

I was overjoyed to receive your kind letter which arrived two days ago on the boat from Miletus. Thank you for all the news from home, and for caring so dutifully for my patients. I really am most grateful.

By the way, I was delighted to learn that Dilean and Rechah had both recovered: I'm most impressed! But you didn't say what had happened to Prochorus. Has his leg mended or is he still paralysed?

Your novel suggestion for a new form of optical poultice was fascinating. I managed to obtain all the ingredients yesterday, and applied it to Paul's eyes this morning: I will let you know if it has any lasting effect on the discharge. The answer to your question is, no, the condition has not existed since birth. It began twenty-three years ago when he was temporarily blinded by a bright light.

Obviously the most important part of your letter was the suggestion you made. I was thunderstruck when I read it. Not because I found it outlandish, as you feared, but because it so closely coincided with my own and Julia's thoughts about the best use of my time while Paul is in prison.

It seems likely now that he's going to be held prisoner in the fortress for many more months. Antonius Felix is reluctant to release him because he's afraid that will infuriate the Jewish authorities. And even *he* cannot condemn Paul when it's so obvious that he's innocent of the charges against him. As you say in your letter, Paul could easily remain prisoner for as long as Felix serves as Governor.

During the last six weeks I've come to realise that I need to discover the truth behind the Jew called Jesus. Julia and her sisters are convinced by the stories they tell me, just as Lydia was. (By the way, I am glad that you've had a long talk with her.) As for myself, I've no idea what the stories mean, but the mere fact that they exist must mean the man was worth knowing.

I recognise that my growing affection for Julia has made me want to impress her with learning and knowledge. But at the same time I am determined to prove her family wrong.

I've had many heated debates with Philip and his four daughters about the Way, and so much of what they say and do makes no sense at all. However, I have been impressed by the actions of the disciples I've met in Caesarea Maritima, for they are the only Jews and Syrians still on speaking terms.

Philip exhausts himself distributing food to the widows and the hungry, as well as comforting those injured or impoverished by the riots. Julia and her sisters sometimes say the most surprising things, and then insist that their god has inspired them.

I've always been fond of Timothy, and Paul is an example

to everybody – obstinate, argumentative, arrogant but convincing. How can anyone be so content when they face such an uncertain future? Yet he cheers me up each morning, debates with Felix once a week, receives a constant stream of visiting disciples, prays unceasingly for all his converts, and dictates complicated letters to people that he's never met. (They're even longer than my last but one to you!)

I've talked to him about your suggestion and he's happy for me to take short periods of leave, as long as I return regularly to Maritima to care for his eyes. What did surprise me was his lack of enthusiasm. He doesn't seem to be interested in learning more about the man's life, as far as he's concerned it's only his alleged return to life that matters!

It's bound to be difficult after twenty-five years to find anyone who can remember the details of what he said. But I hope to establish whether the same stories are told throughout this province, and what they mean for the people today.

I'm leaving at dawn to visit a man called Mnason (I think I've mentioned him already), and then I'm returning to Jerusalem to talk with some Jewish leaders whom Paul thinks once had dealings with Jesus.

I won't be walking to Jerusalem this time, instead I'll be travelling in style. Claudius Lysias has never asked me to return the horse he lent me at the time of our midnight escape, so I can canter round the countryside in comfort.

I promise that I'll write whenever I have news.

With best wishes,

Your loving friend,

Luke.

P.S. Please ask Lydia to send me the manuscript that was circulating in Philippi about six months ago: the one which she said meant so much to her.

Dear Theophilus,

I didn't expect to be writing again so soon, but three days with Mnason have swept away many of my ideas.

Mnason says that Jesus didn't have twelve disciples, that he survived less than two years before being executed, that he was uneducated, that he talked more about money than anything else, and that he was as comfortable lying down at the meal-table as he was standing up in the Temple.

I plan to record everything people tell me about Jesus, but I'll need you to help me understand what their words mean. I'm sure you can remember how, late at night, we used to hammer out lots of new ideas about healing; well, Theo, I need your mind now to help me unravel my thoughts about the Way. I do hope that you'll have enough time for this — but please don't neglect my patients.

Mnason is an ordinary, unrefined person. He's a candlemaker's assistant who joined the Way at the first festival after Jesus' death. He maintains that he heard Jesus speak many times in Jerusalem, but admits that he never saw him work a miracle.

Whenever Lydia or Julia have spoken to me about Jesus they have always described great miracles, and have said that the common people believed he was a god.

Mnason disagrees. He knows the same stories, but insists that they weren't the main cause of Jesus' popularity. He also maintains that these events all took place in the early part of his public life in the north of Palaestina, and that nobody thought he was a god until after the time when he's supposed to have returned to life.

When I arrived here in Antipatris I imagined that Jesus was an educated teacher who rode round the countryside for several years with twelve companions, who healed the sick and did good deeds, who taught people a kinder way of living, who was recognised as one of the gods, who was executed by the Romans, and who was then meant to have returned to life before mysteriously disappearing. Mnason made it plain that it wasn't as simple as that!

He insists that there were nearly a hundred disciples, and that the twelve we've all heard so much about were only close friends from the north who walked south with him to Jerusalem. I argued with him about this, saying that I didn't understand how a false idea could have become so widely accepted.

His answer amused me, for he thought about my question with such a serious expression before saying, 'You can make a spluttering candle from any kind of wax.' It was obviously meant to convey a deep truth which was beyond me!

Anyway, he has given me the name and location of a man in a nearby village who knew the famous Twelve. So I've postponed my trip to Jerusalem and am riding to Emmaus tomorrow.

Wish me well,

Luke.

7th September AD58

Emmaus
Judea
Palaestina

Dear Theophilus,

I've been staying here in Emmaus for the last seven days with the man that Mnason sent me to see – a baker called Cleopas. I'd only planned to spend a day and a night with him, but – like all the disciples I've met so far – he's very hospitable, and he's told me the most astonishing story I've heard in my life.

It's taken me all week to begin to grasp what he's said. And I'm sure that even you, Theo, would be curious to know more.

Lydia's stories about Jesus are all second-hand. Mnason only listened to him from the edge of a crowd. Paul concedes that he's only seen a light and heard a voice. But Cleopas says that he met him, walked with him, ate with him, listened to him, and – wait for this – touched him after he returned to life.

Cleopas explained that he'd been part of a group of Jews who hoped that Jesus would set Palaestina free from Roman rule. Apparently there were several different nationalist groups in the country at that time which all followed whoever was promising to overthrow the Romans.

Cleopas says that some members of his group heard stories coming from the north about a powerful new prophet called Jesus of Nazareth whom some people wanted to make king. When Jesus walked south for Lamb and Unleavened Bread, Cleopas and a friend (now dead) went to meet him at a village outside Jerusalem. They were so impressed by the large number of followers and by the things Jesus said that they decided to join his group.

He says that there were twelve young men called apostles who were Jesus' subordinates, that there was a much bigger group of disciples from the north (he puts his estimate higher than Mnason's, maybe as many as one hundred and fifty), and that there were several hundred, like him, who were enthusiastic new followers from Jerusalem and the surrounding villages.

Every day during the week before the feast, Cleopas and his friend walked seven miles into Jerusalem to hear Jesus speak – and you can imagine how bitterly disappointed they were when he was arrested and executed.

Cleopas insists that the Romans weren't to blame: he maintains that the leaders of Jesus' own people, the Jews, handed him over to be sentenced, and that they had one of their own men killed.

He says that he watched Jesus die on the day before the Sabbath, and that he rested back in Emmaus on the Sabbath. It's the next day, the first day of the week, that's interesting.

Cleopas maintains that he and his friend walked into

Jerusalem to discover what Jesus' subordinates were going to do now that their leader had been killed.

When they reached the house where Jesus' group met, they found them in uproar. Some of the women had been to Jesus' tomb in the early morning and had been unable to find his dead body. They'd returned to the group insisting they'd seen a vision of angels who declared that he was alive.

The group thought that their story was nonsense and would not believe them. However, one of the men ran to the tomb to check, found everything exactly as the women had reported, but saw nothing of Jesus or any angels.

Cleopas told me that some of the group insisted the women had gone to the wrong tomb, whilst others were convinced that the Jewish leaders had stolen the body. He and his friend were so dismayed by this turn of events, and so distressed by the disagreements within the group, that they left Jerusalem for home.

I'm sorry that I've taken so long to get to the point, Theo, but here is Cleopas' amazing story. I think it's best if I give it to you in his own words. This is what he said.

We were walking along the road discussing what had happened in Jerusalem when a stranger caught up with us. He walked with us for about a hundred yards, listening to our conversation; and then he stopped and asked us what we were talking about, and why we were so sad.

I told him that it was none of his business, and tried to walk more quickly to get away from him. I didn't feel like talking to a stranger. But he kept up with our pace and went on asking what was the matter.

In the end I snapped at him, and said that he must be the only person in Jerusalem who didn't know what had been happening.

'What things?' the stranger persisted, 'What has been happening?'

So my friend told him how we'd been hoping that the new prophet from Nazareth would set Palaestina free from the Romans; how we were sad that our leaders had had him killed; and how we'd been astounded by that morning's events.

The stranger called us foolish, and started explaining passages from throughout our Jewish Scriptures which show that our Messiah will suffer before entering his glory.

They do show that, Theo. Cleopas has gone through them with me several times.

The three men had reached Emmaus by the time the stranger had finished speaking, so Cleopas pressed the man to stay with them for the night.

We prepared a meal and then lay down to eat it. Just as we were about to begin eating, the stranger picked up the bread and said the customary blessing. When he'd finished his prayer, he broke the loaf into pieces and handed them to us. It was then – at that precise moment – that we both realised it was Jesus.

Cleopas knows it seems ridiculous that they walked and talked all that way without recognising him. He says he's not sure whether Jesus looked different after his death, or whether their grief and confusion, combined with the fact that they'd never been so close to Jesus before, meant that they just didn't know him.

Anyway, Theo, I've saved the best to last. Cleopas went on to say this: 'The second we recognised him, he vanished. One moment he was eating my best bread, the next he was nowhere to be seen.'

I told him they must have been hallucinating! But he insists there was a half-eaten bread roll on the table!

Cleopas says that he and his friend set out at that instant, and ran the seven miles to Jerusalem to tell the group what had taken place. This is what he said happened next.

> We were exhausted when we got there, and before we
> could regain our breath the apostles had told us that
> Jesus had returned from the dead, and had appeared to
> one of them called Peter.
>
> We amazed them by telling our story and, while
> everybody was talking at the same time, we suddenly
> realised that Jesus was standing among us. He just stood
> there grinning at us, waiting for us to notice him.
>
> The room went deathly quiet. We were terrified,
> and backed away, convinced that we were seeing a
> ghost. So Jesus stretched out his arms and showed us
> the execution wounds on his wrists. Then he sat down,
> took off his sandals, and made us look at his mangled
> feet.
>
> Still none of us believed it was him. So he said he
> was hungry and asked for something to eat – adding
> with a smile, 'Ghosts don't eat!'
>
> One of the women offered him her plate of grilled
> fish, and we were transfixed while we watched him
> swallow the fish and spit out the bones. The moment
> the plate was empty we let out a huge cheer.

Cleopas admitted to me that he's never seen him again, but
all these years later he's still convinced that he saw him. I've
taken him through the story several times a day for seven
days, but I can't shake him. And he won't accept the
possibility that it was an hallucination brought on by grief
and wishful thinking.

I've transcribed what he remembers Jesus saying on the
road. I've questioned him as forcefully as possible without
being rude to a host. And I'm sure that he's telling the truth
as he knows it. Whether or not he did meet Jesus, something
must have happened on that road to explain his devotion to
the Way for the last twenty-five years.

I wish, Theo, that I could convey my excitement at meeting

him. I'm sure it bodes well for my research. Paul will be delighted with the story, and I hope that it makes him feel my absence has been worthwhile.

Please don't mention any of this to Lydia. I want to tell her myself when I see her, I know how she loves these stories.

Tomorrow I ride to Jerusalem to trace the Jewish leaders whose names Paul gave me, and to talk with James about his brother's upbringing and childhood.

Love to everybody,

Luke

14th September AD58

Jerusalem
Judea
Palaestina

Dear Theophilus,

This week has been almost a complete waste of time.

James won't answer any of my questions. And I can't find any of the leaders on Paul's list.

I truly believe that James won't give me any information because he thinks that I'm some sort of spy. He's poor, elderly, uneducated and Jewish. And I suspect that he's got the same problem as the Jews in Maritima of not trusting any educated Greek who can afford to travel on horseback.

I heard that he hadn't joined the Way until after his brother's death. But when I asked him why he hadn't followed Jesus when he was alive, he snapped that it wasn't my business, and said, 'All that matters is I follow him now.'

James came back to me later on, gave me one of his odd stares, and asked, 'If you travel with Paul, why aren't you a disciple?'

I explained that I was his hired physician, and James replied, 'Well, if that's true, why are you here and not with him? And why are you asking so many questions?' As I couldn't think of an intelligent answer, I must have

29

underlined his suspicions.

James let one fact slip. I'd only ever heard Jesus described as coming from Nazareth; so I asked him, if he wouldn't talk to me, whether he would suggest someone in Nazareth who could remember his brother's birth.

He glared at me for a moment, as if in surprise, and then sneered that it was no use me trying my Troatian trick questions on him – and turned to talk to someone else.

I thought about his remark for several days, until I realised that Jesus must have been born somewhere else, and that James thought I knew this and was trying to catch him out.

I've made some enquiries, both with Greek disciples and at the Temple Record Office, and am now certain that Jesus was born six miles south of here in a village called Bethlehem. If I am unable to find any of Paul's contacts in the next few days, I'll ride down there and investigate his background.

With best wishes,

Luke

Dear Theophilus,

Strange things have been happening that I don't understand. As I reported in my last letter, I spent my first seven days in Jerusalem trying to talk to James and to make contact with some of the Jewish leaders.

Nobody would trust me with any information. It was as if James thought I was a spy for the leaders of the Jewish religion, and the leaders thought I was a spy for the Way. Yet I've often heard Paul describe the Way as part of the Jewish religion.

Furthermore, the Jewish leaders loathe Paul and James, even though they're good Jews, and detest all the members of the Way, despite the fact that the Jewish disciples still pray in the Temple, celebrate the sacred feasts, and attend the Sabbath services in the synagogue. It's most puzzling.

However, the attitude of the Jewish leaders changed when they heard that James wouldn't answer my questions. One of them, a man called Eleazar, came to my lodgings and said that a small group would meet me and tell me what they knew.

I've met with them twice now, and the stories they relate are unlike any I've heard before. Lydia wouldn't recognise the man they describe.

Eleazar is a Pharisee (this means that he's part of the group which is the most fervent in keeping the Jewish religious laws). Eleazar says that Jesus was an impostor who tried to mislead the people, an agitator who threatened to destroy the Temple, and a troublemaker who urged the common people to ignore the law and mistrust their chosen leaders.

Eleazar insists that he'd known a man – another Pharisee who's been dead ten years – who had invited Jesus to dine at his house. Apparently Jesus sat down without washing when he arrived, and launched into an insulting attack on his host.

Eleazar's face turned quite white when he was telling me what Jesus had said. His tight lips quivered and his shrill voice rose as he recited Jesus' words to his host.

'You fool!' Jesus shouted, 'You're full to the top with extortion and wickedness. Why do you go on neglecting justice and the love of God? Do you know what you're like? I'll tell you anyway – one of those unmarked tombs which defile people when they touch them by accident.'

Theo my friend, you should have heard the venom in Eleazar's voice as he spoke. Do you remember the man we treated last year who believed that he'd been poisoned by his neighbour? It was like that, yet worse.

One of Eleazar's companions maintains that he knew an

expert on the Jewish law who'd been at that meal, and he says this lawyer told him he'd rebuked Jesus for being so insulting.

But apparently Jesus turned on the lawyer and accused him – and all lawyers – of loading burdens on the common people which they wouldn't touch with their own fingertips.

There was more, much more, and I've written it all down. Even if it's only half true, it begins to explain the bad feeling between the Way and the Jewish leaders. But what I don't understand is why Jesus was so angry with these people: they all seem very religious to me.

I've told Eleazar that I'd like to speak to a Pharisee who had dealings with Jesus in person. He's promised to produce one soon, so I'm going to stay here for another week before riding to Beth-lehem.

I do hope that when I return to Caesarea Maritima there'll be a thick wad of letters which are packed with details about my patients' progress. I need the refreshment of news from home, and I need the instruction of your insight.

Your good friend,

Luke

25th September AD58

Jerusalem
Judea
Palaestina

Dear Theophilus,
This is much more difficult than I imagined it would be. On each of the last five days Eleazar has brought a different elderly Pharisee to my room.

They've all testified that Jesus of Nazareth was a liar, a rogue and a false prophet. But I don't think that any of them ever met him in person. They all speak about what this Pharisee knew, what that lawyer thought, and what Rabbi so-and-so said.

It's extraordinary. They all hate Jesus. Do you understand

me? They hate him as much as Lydia loves him. Even though it's twenty-five years since he died, it's as though he had spat in their faces a few hours ago. They've sat opposite me with their knees pressed together, their hands clenched tight, and hatred written all over their faces.

Yet I've a growing suspicion they only dislike him because he was so popular with the common people, because he broke the rules of public debating, and because he came from a part of their country which is despised by the educated classes of Southern Palaestina. I know it doesn't seem enough to explain their loathing, but I can't think of a better explanation.

Julia has often told me that Jesus was a wonderful teacher who taught with more authority than all the scribes and Pharisees put together. And I remember her saying that he told amusing stories which penetrated deeper than a gladiator's sword.

One of these men related a story which he insisted Jesus told to a group of Pharisees. It had outraged them, and this man clearly only related it to shock me. I ruined the interview by laughing: Eleazar was disgusted with me!

The story was about two men who went to the Jerusalem Temple to pray: one was a Pharisee and the other was a tax collector. What annoyed them so much was Jesus' assertion that only the tax collector came out forgiven by God!

Theo, you should have been there when the indignant old Pharisee told this story. His eyes bulged and his stringy neck vibrated so much that he looked like a half-starved chicken! I guarantee that you'd have been unable to keep a straight face.

If Jesus told it half as well as he, it's little wonder he was popular with the common people – and even less wonder that the religious leaders hated him.

I told Eleazar this morning to stop wasting my time with second-hand stories and threatened that, unless he produced an authentic eye-witness soon, I would go home and tell all Macedonia that the opponents of the Way in Jerusalem were all puff and no substance!

I hope that you're still looking after my patients with skill and devotion, but that you haven't let them forget whose patients they are.

Best wishes,
Your loving friend, Luke.

2nd October AD58

Jerusalem
Judea
Palaestina

Dear Theophilus,

I've been waiting a whole week for Eleazar to produce a Pharisee who disputed in person with Jesus. He promises that a man called Simon will visit me soon, but he lives in a town which is several days journey to the north. Eleazar says he's sent word, and insists that he's coming: in the meantime I learn patience, shape questions, and think of Philippi.

I haven't been entirely wasting my time, for I've visited every inn in Jerusalem asking anyone who was healed by Jesus to come forward for examination.

There have been the inevitable tricksters who'll say anything in the hope of payment: most have gone away muttering complaints about Greeks when I've made it plain that I'm not offering money. A few have insisted that he healed their ailments, but their stories haven't stood up to my detailed cross examination.

One man has been helpful. In fact the more I think about his testimony the more I'm sure that it's genuine. Parts of it are similar to other stories I've heard, but my main reason for trusting him is that he's neither a disciple nor a Pharisee. He treasures the memory of his meeting with Jesus, yet seems to be sad that he's not lived by his words.

He came to see me two days ago and only agreed to talk to me on the understanding that I didn't ask his name. He told me about a meal which took place on a Sabbath in the house of a leading Pharisee – he wouldn't say which one. Many distinguished guests were present who were all watching Jesus closely, and one of them suffered from dropsy.

My visitor insists that as soon as Jesus noticed the man, he asked the guests whether it was lawful to heal on the Sabbath. There was complete silence. Nobody could look Jesus in the eye. After looking steadily round the room, Jesus took the man, cured him, and sent him away.

You can imagine the questions I asked. 'Which incantations did he utter?' 'What potion did he give?' 'Which instruments did he use?'

But my visitor had no answers: he simply maintained that it had all happened so quickly that nobody had noticed how he'd cured him. He just says that the guest walked in as fat as a pregnant camel and walked out as thin as a rabbi's staff. It's infuriating that the man died eight years ago and can't be examined.

I asked my visitor what occurred after the healing, and he gave me a detailed answer which I've transcribed. But the gist is that Jesus lectured the guests on humility.

One thing I must tell you is that he remembers Jesus rebuking the host for inviting the wrong people. Apparently Jesus called out, 'Listen to me everyone! Next time you arrange a party don't invite your neighbours and rich relations. Invite the poor, the crippled, the lame and the blind instead.'

This must have been bothering my visitor for twenty-five years because he kept on asking me whether I thought it was right. 'Should he have said such a thing?' he enquired. 'Do you think it's good advice?' he went on. And he must have asked me a dozen times what Jesus really meant.

It sounded like appalling advice to me, so I said that physicians saw so many cripples during the day that the last thing they wanted to do was eat with them at night.

But it's irritated me, Theo, like a splinter which is too

deep to remove. Whenever I've given a party in Philippi I've never dreamt of inviting the poor. Why, I've only ever eaten with people from my own group, with people like you and Achaicus. I'd never ask anyone to my table who couldn't return my invitation or use my services.

I've had many disagreements with Lydia about this very matter. The poor are always lying at her table, and I've often rebuked her for setting such a dreadful example.

All the disciples I've met seem to care more for the poor and the crippled than for their own flesh and blood! It seems wrong, but – as I said – his words are digging into my mind like a thorn in a dog's paw.

If one of his second-hand sayings can affect me so deeply, I suppose I shouldn't be surprised to find that the people who heard him in person reacted so strongly.

My visitor told me that Jesus related another one of his pointed stories at the end of the meal.

What happened is that one of the men at the meal made the sort of ridiculous comment people make in long silences – something about how lucky are those who'll share a meal with God. My visitor says that, at this, Jesus sat bolt upright and told them a story about a man who was planning a banquet.

It went like this: a certain man invited a large number of friends who all made excuses and offered apologies for not attending. But the excuses my visitor recalled Jesus giving were completely unreasonable – nobody in their right mind would miss a free banquet for the reasons he gave.

Anyway, the story continued: the host flew into a rage and ordered his servant to go out to the streets and alleys to bring in the poor, the crippled, the lame and so on. When he'd done this there were still empty spaces, so the host sent his servant out to the countryside to urge strangers to come to his banquet.

My visitor says that Jesus was silent for a moment; then he looked round, told the guests that not one of those who were invited would taste a morsel of the man's banquet, lay back down again, and seemed quite unaware of the upset he'd caused.

He's clearly been troubled by his story ever since. (I guess he was the guest whose comment prompted the story.) And he's worried that he won't have a place at God's meal.

I didn't know what to say. I thought about sending him to one of the disciples, but in the end I prescribed him a potion to make him sleep without dreaming.

Paul wants me back in Maritima by the end of this month so I must press on with my research. I'm ending now as it's almost too dark to write – I could do with some of Mnason's spluttering candles!

With best wishes,

Luke

8th October AD58

Beth-lehem
Judea
Palaestina

Dear Theophilus,

I gave up on Eleazar five days ago and rode to Beth-lehem to see if I could discover anything here.

Nothing!

I must have knocked on every door in the town asking for someone who could remember Jesus' birth.

Nobody!

I know that it must have been at least sixty years ago so the chances of finding a witness are slight, but I'm still disappointed by my failure.

In one inn there was an ancient shepherd (he must have told me a dozen times that he was eighty-three) who tried to convince me that he'd seen an angel when he was working one night as a youth! He reckons that the angel told him he'd find the Jewish Messiah if he looked for a baby in a Beth-lehem cow shed!

37

He says that he and some of his friends went down to the village and found a baby where the angel had said. But he didn't know its name or what happened to it – he said its parents were strangers passing through. He's old and feeble, so he probably only told me what he thought I wanted to hear in the hope of a drink!

I don't want to return to Jerusalem with blank parchments, so I've written down everything he said. But I doubt whether his rambling thoughts are anything to do with Jesus.

I'm convinced that I'll have to head north to find useful information. I'm going to try my luck here for a few more days, then head slowly back to Maritima.

Yours,

Luke

13th October AD58   Jerusalem
Judea
Palaestina

Dear Theophilus,

I returned here two days ago to find an abrupt note from Eleazar which stated that his prize witness had arrived, and would I please hurry and interview him as he was bearing the cost of his lodgings! I was tempted to ride back to Bethlehem for a few more days, but curiosity triumphed over mischief so I invited Simon around straight away.

He's not like the other Pharisees that I've met in Jerusalem, and has little of the stiffnecked self-importance of Eleazar's companions: maybe it's because he's lived all his life in Ginae (a town in the north of this province). I liked Simon. Although he's not part of the Way, he doesn't appear hostile to Jesus.

Living in the north, Simon heard rumours about a new prophet earlier than the southern Pharisees. He says that several synagogue officials had come to him with reports of devils fleeing from women, with stories of lame men walking, and even with news of a dead son returning to life in the next town. (Yes, Theo, I did remember to check which town and where.)

Simon says that most of his colleagues didn't approve of Jesus eating with tax collectors or healing on the Sabbath, but that he wanted to meet Jesus and decide for himself whether he was a true prophet. So Simon invited Jesus to a private meal with his family. This is what Simon says took place, in his own words:

> Jesus agreed to come, and when he arrived he took his place lying at my table. The meal had just begun when a woman burst into the room clutching a jar of ointment. I didn't know her name, but I recognised her as someone with a terrible reputation in the town.

(Theo, I'll leave you to guess what Simon said she was famous for!)

> She stood sobbing behind Jesus, and some of her tears fell on his feet. But instead of asking my wife for a towel, she bent down and dried his feet with her hair! Then she broke down completely, smothered Jesus' feet with her kisses, and poured her ointment all over them. The room stank.
>
> I didn't know what to do. I didn't want to offend a guest. I just wanted the woman out of my house as quickly as possible. I was about to order a servant to remove her when I suddenly remembered that I'd asked Jesus for the meal to find out whether he was a prophet.
>
> That made me smile, for the awful woman had solved my problem. If Jesus was a true prophet he'd have known what she was, and wouldn't have let her touch him.
>
> This was all going through my mind when Jesus spoke up. He told me a story which – at first – made

me carry on smiling: it was too ridiculous for words. It was about a banker who had two men in his debt. One owed £500, the other £50. They were unable to pay, so Jesus said that he let them both off.

When he'd finished telling his story, Jesus asked me which one would have loved the banker the most, and I gave him the obvious answer.

Then he wiped the smile off my face by turning to the woman, and telling me that she had more love than me. He didn't look at me, he just carried on gazing at the woman. He said that I hadn't washed his feet, or kissed him in greeting, or anointed him with oil.

It was all true. I hadn't done any of those things, but only because I'd wanted to test him. However, he'd turned the tables, and had shamed me in front of my family.

When Jesus stopped speaking he turned round and looked at me. His dark eyes locked on to mine, and he smiled a sad little smile. I can still remember the look in his eyes, for one moment it made me feel like kneeling and asking his forgiveness. But I couldn't do such a thing in front of that woman.

It doesn't end there, Theo. Before Simon could recover his composure he heard Jesus telling the woman that her sins were forgiven. This was too much for Simon. He says that he could accept Jesus as a prophet, he could recognise the unusual depth of his love, but no man, *no* man (I can still see him shaking his head) could forgive sins except God.

I can't have questioned Simon very well because there are a few things in my notes which I don't understand. But even so, he's given me more insight into Jesus than anyone I've spoken to yet.

Simon believes that Jesus was a genuinely good man who went too far. He's convinced that he did work miracles (he says that he investigated a few himself) and that he did help the common people live better lives. But he thinks that Jesus gave in to the pressure of the crowds and said things which no man should say.

At one stage I wanted to interrupt him and say, 'Suppose he was right? Suppose he could forgive sins?' But Simon was too nice to disturb any more. I think he's been in turmoil since the meal, wanting to believe that Jesus was special, yet frightened at what it would mean for his life.

There's not much more for me to do here, so I'll probably say farewell to the leaders of the Way tomorrow, to Eleazar the day after, and then ride back to Philip's house – though I might call in at Mnason's on the way.

I'm looking forward to reading your letters and hearing that all my patients have dramatically recovered!

With best wishes,

Your loving friend,

Luke

18th October AD58

Antipatris
Samaria
Palaestina

Dear Theophilus,

Mnason tells me that seven weeks have passed since I was last at his table. It doesn't seem that long, but when we started talking I realised how much had happened.

When I was here before, Mnason confused me with what he said about Jesus: now he's helping me make sense of some of the things that puzzled me in Jerusalem.

He's explained how many disciples have been imprisoned, beaten and killed, and how many times the Jewish leaders have tried to plant spies and buy traitors in the Way. He says it's a miracle that James is still alive, and that he's under constant attack from the authorities just because he's Jesus' brother. The High Priest has twice threatened him with stoning.

Mnason also tells me that he would have written a letter of introduction if he'd known I was going to question James. I could have wrung his neck when he said that — especially since I'm sure I did tell him! Think what trouble such a letter would have saved.

What Mnason can't explain to my satisfaction is why the Pharisees are so hostile to Jesus. I can understand them envying Jesus' popularity, resenting his lack of formal education, and being jealous of the way he worked miracles. But once they'd had him killed, I'd have thought that would have ended the matter.

Why are they still so angry? And why do they want to erase his memory from the Empire? They're foolish really, for the strength of their opposition only draws attention to his cause. I'm starting to think that he must have been either an evil deceiver who deserved their opposition, or such a good man that they were ashamed by his behaviour.

Mnason just says it was written in the Scriptures that the Messiah would suffer, so he had to. Perhaps he's right. But does any of it make sense to you, Theo? Can you see a meaning in all this confusion? Is there an explanation that I've missed?

Mnason was surprised to learn that I'd heard Cleopas' story. He says that I was greatly honoured because life has been so difficult for the disciples in Samaria they usually consider it prudent not to describe their experiences to outsiders.

He's advised me to be careful when I relate it in case the authorities take action to silence Cleopas. His warnings have made me regret the foolish way I threatened Eleazar: Mnason insists that he's more dangerous than he appears.

I trust that you're well. Please pass on my greetings to Lydia, and to all those in Philippi who can still remember me. I've almost forgotten what your dispensary looks like!

With best wishes,
Your friend,

Luke.

Dear Theo,   19 Oct AD 58.

Just arrived back!
The Miletus boat leaves in a
few minutes, so I've only time
enough to thank you for the
letters. Julia says that there are
five from you and two from Lydia.
Everybody seems well though I've
no news of Paul.
I'll write a full letter when I've
digested your news.
                    Yours
                         Luke.

POST CARD

His 7
The S
Phys
Philip
Maed

Caesarea Maritima, Samaria, Palaestina

Dear Theophilus,

I'm sorry that it's been so long since I last wrote, especially as I devoured your five letters which awaited my return from Jerusalem. It was very thoughtful to include those extracts from the *City Journal*, and thank you for taking the trouble to send so much information about my patients.

What excellent news about Prochorus' leg – and about Janus' stomach! I always find that cakes of dried figs stop stomach complaints. But I was saddened to read of Fortunatus' death: he'd been a good friend. I'm sure you did all you could to ease his passing.

So Lois did have twin boys after all! I'd like to congratulate her in person, but I'm glad not to have to hear Melech's boasting. Remind him from me that it's the first time he's been right in two years.

I was amazed to read that Timon's household have had the gall to come back to you for more treatment. After all they said when their maid died! Charge them double!

Enough of that. I must confess that, at first, I was frustrated when your letters didn't answer some of my questions. But then I remembered how long it takes for correspondence to travel by sea. So for the last three weeks I've been standing in the crowd on the harbour wall each time the Miletus boat has sailed in, hoping for another letter. Two have arrived, but I've still not received your reply to the one I sent from Antipatris.

When I came home empty-handed today I decided that I shouldn't wait any longer: it was time to sharpen my quill and bring you up to date with my news.

Paul was very pleased by my return as he'd dismissed the local physician whom I'd hired to care for his eyes in my absence – and then he'd had to ask Philip to cleanse them instead. They'd stopped using the optical poultice you recommended because Paul complained that it irritated him.

Would you believe it? The man can endure a flogging but can't bear a poultice!

I've ignored his complaints and have been applying it vigorously since I returned. The discharge has already decreased, but it may be due to the colder weather.

Paul wanted to hear all about my research, and wasn't surprised to learn that I hadn't been trusted by James. Paul told me that the leaders of the Way in Jerusalem thought *he* was a spy when he became a disciple twenty-three years ago.

I asked him why the Pharisees had always hated Jesus – and soon regretted it, for he gave me a long and complicated lecture about 'faith'. It's one of his favourite words!

I'm not sure if I understood him correctly, but I think I got the gist. Paul says the Pharisees are cocksure that they're God's chosen people, and are convinced that they are pure and blameless because they give one tenth of everything to the priests (even their herbs), and are certain that they've a special calling to persuade others to keep all the small details of the Jewish religious law – plus new ones they invent by the hour.

Whereas Paul says Jesus taught that God's love and forgiveness are given freely to all who'll accept them – not just to a chosen few, but to sinners, tax collectors, defiled women and non-Jews. (Paul paused dramatically before leaning forward and giving extra emphasis to those last two words. I ignored his bait, so he added with a loud grunt, 'And pagan physicians too'!)

Paul insists that Jesus was more concerned with people's inner attitudes than their external actions. Apparently he was forever calling the Pharisees 'a bunch of hypocrites' because they were more interested in the correct way to wash their own clean hands than in caring for the sick, feeding the hungry, forgiving debts, and clothing the poor.

I couldn't resist teasing Paul about my research. On the first day I told him about everyone except Cleopas. On the second day I said that I'd remembered one more minor incident!

He was so excited that he made up a hymn about the story (not a very good one) and sang it to me the next day. He's asked me a different question about Cleopas every day since.

Paul tells me that he collects stories about the meetings people had with Jesus after his death, and that this is his first new one in nearly ten years. I haven't dared read him your comments and questions about Cleopas' account – he'd ban me from corresponding with you!

There still looks to be no end to Paul's imprisonment, and Paul says that Antonius Felix is unlikely to release him before the feast of Lamb and Unleavened Bread next April. So it looks as though you'll be tending my patients for another six months. How will I ever be able to repay you?

Philip and his family have made me most welcome in their home again. Philip treats me like a son, and the four girls care for me with great tenderness: why, Julia admitted how much she'd missed me and that she'd prayed every day for my safety!

They've told me they believe it's important that Jesus' teachings are written down before the witnesses die or disperse across the Empire. Philip sat me down two weeks ago and told me that he'd given the matter serious thought, and had concluded that it was better for an honest outsider to research and write them, than for a member of the Way. He thinks that people of other nations are more likely to trust such an account. I agree with that.

I told him that I was only researching Jesus' teaching for my own education and for yours, Theo. (I couldn't say I was doing it to prove him wrong!) But that only made him even more certain I was the right person. He and his daughters seem convinced that I'm meant to make my findings widely available: they actually think that Paul is in prison just so that I can write an ordered account of the whole story right from the beginning! I hope he didn't tell Paul that!

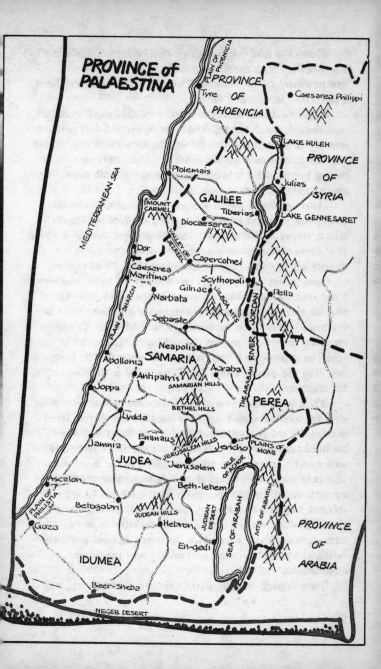

Philip has told me everything that he knows, and some of his experiences in the years after Jesus' death are so extraordinary that I would not have believed them had I not known him as well as I do.

Lydia explained in her second letter that there were two manuscripts which she believed to be accurate: I only remember hearing extracts read from the one by Quartus, I don't think she can have shown me the other account. Anyway, I wrote asking her to hire a scribe to make copies of both manuscripts, and to forward them as quickly as possible.

However, I foolishly neglected to explain how she should pay. Theo my good friend, please sell some of my effects which you've stored and give her the proceeds to pay a scribe. If she's not chosen one yet, hire the man who sits in the Square outside the Council Chamber. He is to be trusted.

Your letters comment on my findings up to Beth-lehem. I've noted all your observations and suggestions, and agree that discovering the answers to these six questions must be my priority: (i) What happened to his body? (ii) What methods did he use to heal the sick? (iii) Where did he go when he disappeared? (iv) Where and when was he born? (v) Why did people follow him? (vi) What is the meaning of his teachings?

Then, with regard to some of the other points you made. (i) I enclose the sketch map of Palaestina which you asked for. (ii) I'll do as you suggest and try to find some other members of his family – although it's surely unlikely that either of his parents are still alive. (iii) I agree that I must ride north when Paul next allows me to be absent for two months. (iv) I'll remember to check the official Empire records. (v) I won't forget to ask about his ideas on wealth. (I accept your rebuke that I'd overlooked this aspect of Mnason's testimony.) And (vi) I'm sorry that I'd neglected to tell you what happened to Timothy and the other companions.

They arrived from Jerusalem three days after Paul and

myself, and Paul sent them off on the first boat north to take instructions and news to different groups of disciples. Timothy and Gaius went to Galatia; Trophimus and Tychicus were sent to West Asia; and the others sailed back to Macedonia.

I think that's exhausted everything.

With best wishes,

Your grateful friend,

Luke.

27th December AD58   **Caesarea Maritima**
                                              Samaria

Dear Theophilus,   **Palaestina**

Greetings, my good friend. Five weeks ago there was another outbreak of severe rioting, and I was dragged from my horse and beaten by a crowd of Jews. My right arm was badly injured, and has taken all this time to heal: Julia has renamed me 'Luke the left-handed', and Paul has been feeling the effects as I've tended his eyes more clumsily than usual.

Antonius Felix has executed the worst rioters, and has sent the two sets of ringleaders to Rome for the Emperor to settle their dispute about the settlers' civil privileges. The authorities were so desperate for medical help that they gave me a generous payment to help tend the wounded: it was good to use my cack-handed skills on something more complicated than Paul's incurable eye problem.

The city soon settled down after the executions, and my life slipped into a fixed pattern, with each day like the one before. I rise at dawn, care for my horse, break my fast, and then ride to the fortress to attend to Paul's needs. I cleanse his eyes, converse with him, read him any letters that have come from disciples around the Empire (he can only read large script unaided), and return to my room to struggle with Aramaic.

All the educated people in Palaestina are fluent in Greek, so I had few difficulties making myself understood in Jerusalem, and have none here in the capital. Philip insists that it will be different in the north. I've been eager to start on my next journey, but he maintains that I'm not ready.

I have spent each afternoon interviewing a steady stream of disciples about the history of the Way. Julia's sisters have arranged for three different disciples to visit me each day. I've asked them all the questions you suggested, plus many more of my own, and Julia has transcribed their answers while I've been unable to write. (You should see her writing; it's outstanding for a woman – the best I've come across.)

The disciples have all been surprised to be asked why they started to follow Jesus: it's as though they think the answer is self-evident. When they've thought about the question for a few minutes they've said things like, 'He was our friend,' or, 'We wanted to be close to him,' or, 'He understood us,' or, 'Nobody had cared for us before,' or, 'He filled us with such joy.'

They've all been shocked (some have even been upset) to be asked what difference he's made to their lives. 'Do you really need to ask?' they say. 'Isn't it obvious?' they protest. I think they feel that they're boasting and this makes them uncomfortable, but eventually they've pointed to the way they share their food and resources with the poor, to their readiness to care for the sick and strangers, to their affection for people from other races, and to their own sense of joy and forgiveness. 'We feel loved,' they say, 'so we love in return.' 'He's given us everything,' they smile, 'so we give as much as we can'.

It's been strangely moving, and most endearing. So much so that I've started joining them on the evening of the first day of the week. That's when they gather in each other's homes to eat, to remember his life and death, to sing praises, and to pray for each other. These have been precious times: I know it's a strange thing to write, Theo, but it's as though

I've been cleansed by their friendship. You won't understand that, but I can't put it any other way.

Enough of my foolish sentiment. Paul has finally given me permission to be absent for two months. Philip says that my Aramaic is not good enough for the journey, but I'm going anyway. Julia has promised to pray every day for my success and my safety. My horse is fit and strong. So I'll be off for the north and for Galilee in five days time.

Philip will care for Paul in my place, and Paul has agreed to write some letters on my behalf to disciples who may be able to help with the research. He says that he knows a man called Manaen who is the foster brother of Herod Antipas (he ruled Galilee and Perea during Jesus' lifetime). Apparently this man was brought up with Herod, but then left him to become a disciple, and is now a leader of the Way in the province of Syria.

I'm taking my quills, Theo, so I'll write regularly while I'm away. Please reply with more of your comments and questions, and please encourage Lydia to write as well. I know she finds it difficult, but I'd like to hear from her again.

Pass on my greetings to all my patients – especially to Lois and to Fortunatus' three sons – and tell them I'll be home by mid-summer.

With best wishes,
Your left-handed friend,   *Luke.*

P.S. I hope you remembered to sell some of my effects and hire a scribe. I need those manuscripts.

Dear Theophilus,

When I finally fell asleep yesterday evening, I was more exhausted and saddle-sore than at any stage since my midnight escape from Jerusalem.

It would only take a hooded crow a few hours to fly the forty miles from Caesarea Maritima to here. But it took me all day, even though I must have followed the crow's route, for a new Roman road runs straight across the countryside without a curve to the left or the right.

I left Philip's house at dawn yesterday and rode for eight miles over the plains. The road then steepened and roughened as it followed the winding Iron Hills Pass up through the Carmel mountains then down to Capercotnei – where the Maximianpolis Legion is garrisoned against a rebellion in Galilee. I rested there several hours as my horse had found the mountain crossing difficult. The new road continued straight onwards from there, across the wide Jezreel valley to Gabatha, where again I paused to rest and water my horse. After leaving Gabatha the road climbed through the hills of Lower Galilee. I turned off at dusk to ride into Diocaesarea, which is the chief city of all Galilee, arriving at this inn just after nightfall, unsure whether I or my horse was the more tired.

The Jews call this city Sepphoris, and I shall make enquiries here for a few days before riding west to Lake Gennesaret, where most of the stories are based.

Philip was right! I am having more problems with the language. But it's not the Galileans who can't make out my poor, broken Aramaic, it's me who can't understand their rough accents.

My letters will take even longer to reach you from here – they have to go all the way back to Maritima to catch the Miletus boat.

Best wishes,

Luke.

Dear Theophilus,

It's already clear that this is going to be fertile ground for research. Almost everybody I've spoken to over the age of forty has a story to tell about the events which took place here thirty years ago.

The outline is clear. Jesus lived in Nazareth (that's a village four miles south-east of here) with his family until he was aged about thirty.

Then he left home to visit a relative who was teaching further south down the Jordan valley. He returned after a few months a changed person. He stopped working, started healing, and began speaking in local synagogues. His teaching was unusual, amusing and authoritative: ordinary people easily understood him.

People recall that Jesus was always asking them to think about things in a new way: my innkeeper gave me an example. He described the local population's anger when Pontius Pilate (he was the Roman Governor of Palaestina at that time) executed some Galileans when they were in the middle of making their religious sacrifices.

A deputation went to Jesus, reported the incident, and asked him to explain it. He couldn't. Instead he commented that they hadn't died in such tragic circumstances because they were sinners; then he frightened the deputation by stabbing his finger at them, and saying, 'Unless you start thinking differently, you'll perish like they did.'

There must have been something special about Jesus. Even though he said frightening things like that, people here confess that they looked forward to listening to him. Many admit that he changed the way they thought; yet it doesn't seem to have lasted. There are fond memories here, but no members of the Way.

One rumour I heard is that the people of Nazareth threw him out of their synagogue and tried to kill him. Somebody said that this was why he moved his base to a village called Capernaum.

I rode to Nazareth yesterday to question its inhabitants. Most were reluctant to talk about the rumour, but one group of old people admitted it was true and gave me the details.

They owned up to their surprise when Jesus stopped working. 'When he grew up among us he seemed perfectly normal,' they said. 'We'd looked after him. We'd given him work. So he shouldn't have gone off without saying a word to anyone,' they complained. And one man told me, 'We could hardly believe it was him when he came back. He'd never said things like that before.'

What upset them most was Jesus' assertion that Jewish prophets were never accepted in their own home town. 'That's what made us angry,' they spat. 'Who did he think he was – making wild claims about himself and criticising his neighbours before they had done anything?' These men thought that Jesus had slurred both them and the town which had raised him.

I asked after his parents: at first nobody would tell me anything, but eventually one old man said that he thought Jesus' mother was still alive.

I couldn't believe my ears! At first I thought that I must have misunderstood him, and pressed him hard. It was so difficult. His dreadful Galilean accent and my broken Aramaic meant our conversation was slower than a lame camel. He insisted that he didn't know where she was living, but at least this has given me hope. I shall ask after her wherever I go. Why didn't James or any of the Jerusalem disciples tell me about her?

Incidentally, Theo, these letters won't take so long to reach you after all. I've learnt that there's another new road which goes north-west from here straight to Ptolemais in the province of Phoenicia. My innkeeper says that the port is only seventeen miles away – I'd no idea it was so near.

With best wishes,

Luke.

Dear Theophilus,
At last!

At long, long last, after almost five months of searching, I've found and examined someone who was healed by Jesus.

I rode here two days ago, fully intending only to spend one night in Taricheae before riding on to Capernaum. It's the regional centre and, like most of the major towns, has several names: most Jews call it Magdala, but the Romans renamed it in their campaign to Romanise even the remotest parts of the Empire.

I took lodgings and, after I'd stabled my horse, lay down for supper. The elderly innkeeper enquired about my business (I don't think he has many visitors) and I told him that I was a Macedonian physician who was seeking to establish the truth about Jesus of Nazareth.

He laughed and said he could tell that I wasn't one of his disciples. This puzzled me, and I asked him how he could know. 'Your horse!' he laughed, 'Your horse!' The questioning look on my face made him continue, and he explained that he'd never met a disciple who'd owned a horse.

He went on to tell me that he'd liked Jesus, had listened to him, and had wanted to follow him. But Jesus' insistence that his followers give everything to the poor had been too extreme. He said that most Galileans would have followed Jesus to Jerusalem and back if he hadn't made it so hard to be a disciple.

We talked until the candle burnt down, and, just as I was about to retire for the night, I said that my real hope as a physician was to meet someone who'd been healed by Jesus.

He banged down his pot, slapped me on the shoulder, and boomed, 'Why didn't you say so earlier?' Then he burst out laughing and disappeared into the kitchen.

He returned with his wife. 'Here's who you've been

looking for,' he said, 'I only married her because she was healed.' Then he turned to his wife, lit a new candle, and ordered her to tell me her story.

It was all too much for me that first evening, and I could hardly sleep for excitement. The next day I persuaded the wife to repeat her story so that I could transcribe it, and managed to convince her husband that I should be permitted to examine her.

Theo, it's remarkable. They say that she'd been bent double for eighteen years and unable to stand upright. One Sabbath, Jesus visited their synagogue, saw her, called her over, and announced, 'Woman, you are free from your disability.'

They swear that's all he said. No incantation, no spell, no charm, nothing like that at all!

Then he gently touched her; and she says that she immediately straightened up and began to praise God.

There's no evidence now of any physical deformity, and they've introduced me to a score of people who testify to the truth of the story. They all remember it well because Jesus called the synagogue president a hypocrite when he told the woman that she shouldn't have been healed on the Sabbath.

I asked the innkeeper how he thought Jesus had done it, and he maintained that it's because he was a prophet. He explained that his God gives a spirit to prophets which helps them work miracles. It was all very confusing, partly because he was talking too fast so I had to keep on reminding him to speak slower because I didn't understand much Aramaic.

I think he said that his God gave Jesus a spirit while he was visiting a relative in the Jordan valley, and that this is why Jesus came back so different. I'll need to think about that for a lot longer!

I asked the couple why they aren't members of the Way. They say that they still attend the synagogue every Sabbath, but that they don't believe he returned from the dead and that they aren't so stupid as to give everything they possess to the poor.

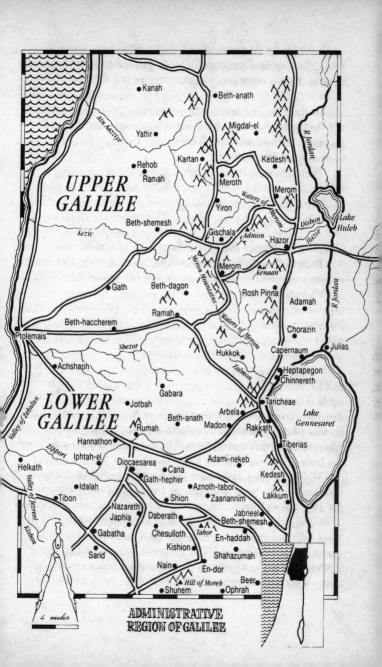

ADMINISTRATIVE
REGION OF GALILEE

Theo, can you guess what I did? I told them Cleopas' story: that made them think! I'm so pleased to have met this couple, yet am strangely sad that they're not members of the Way.

In the past I've asked you not to tell Lydia about some of my findings: please tell her about this couple, and beg her to pray that they join the Way.

Love to everybody,

Your friend,

Luke.

P.S. The innkeeper has an excellent map of Galilee which was left behind by a Roman road-making team. I made two exact copies so here's one of them; now you can follow my Galilean travels more easily.

17th January AD59

Capernaum
Lower Galilee
Palaestina

Dear Theophilus,

Do you remember me telling you how Mnason insisted that Jesus had more than twelve disciples? He thought that Cleopas had been one of them, but in fact he'd been a follower for only a few days before Jesus' death.

Well, here in Capernaum I've found a group of disciples who've been meeting together on the first day of the week for twenty-five years, and several of them have been disciples from the very first months of Jesus' public ministry!

I left Taricheae three days ago (the innkeeper shouted down the road after me, 'You'll have to get rid of that horse if you want to be a disciple!') and rode six miles round the edge of Lake Gennesaret to this village. It was a beautiful clear day and I could see the hills eight miles away on the other side of the lake.

The first person I spoke to directed me to the house of a man called Dedan. When he realised that I was Paul's private physician you would have thought that Nero himself had arrived at his door.

I've often noted the lavish hospitality shown by the disciples, but Dedan outshines them all. My only reservation is that he serves fish at every meal, but that is his trade, so I shouldn't complain.

I suspect he thinks his God has sent me so that he can recount every detail of his life from his birth until the present day! But in truth he has been remarkably helpful in checking my notes. Several times he's told me that I've not got a story or a teaching quite right, and has explained to me what Jesus meant.

I've learnt that Jesus chose Dedan, his elder brother Sheba (now dead) and seventy other disciples, and sent them ahead of him in pairs to the towns and villages that he planned to visit.

Dedan has repeated the instructions Jesus gave them: they had to follow a spartan existence – no horses or home comforts for them! But the most extraordinary fact of all is that Jesus told them to cure the sick themselves. And Dedan says that they could, and that devils submitted to them when they used Jesus' name!

He insists that they didn't use charms or spells or any magical practices. 'Just his name' Dedan says, 'Just his name!'

Can you believe it, Theo? One word, and they could ward off devils!

I've always thought that Paul was teasing me when he's said he's sometimes been able to heal the sick. ('Go on then!' I've always snapped back. 'Open your eyes and stop them discharging.') But this is the first time I've come across an uneducated disciple who's made a similar claim.

Dedan has given me enough material to fill two packs of parchments, but he's added only one new pointed story to my collection. He heard Jesus tell it to an expert on the Jewish law who was trying to test him, and it's a cutting indictment of the religious leaders.

This time the hero isn't a tax collector or a sinner, it's a generous foreigner. And Jesus ended the story by telling the lawyer to behave like the foreigner. You know enough Jews, Theo, to realise what a shock that must have been! It made a great impression on Dedan, and he says that he's been trying to live like the foreigner for twenty-six years.

I've been so busy transcribing Dedan's words that I've not had time to meet anyone else. I'm staying here for a few more days to interview the other long-term disciples, and to eat with them all on the first day of the week. Then I'm going to escape from Dedan and research more freely in the surrounding small villages.

I hope that you are still well, and still visiting Lydia – please give her my love.

With best wishes,
Your good friend,

Luke.

27th January AD59

Julias
Gaulanitis
Palaestina

Dear Theophilus,
Hasn't this town got a beautiful Roman name! The local people call it Bethsaida, and although it's on the edge of Lake Gennesaret it's not part of the administrative region of Galilee. When I crossed the River Jordan two-and-a-half miles east of Capernaum, I passed out of Antonius Felix's control and into the territory still ruled by King Agrippa II.

During the last week I've visited the villages of Chorazin, Adamah, Rosh Pinna, Hukkok, Chinnereth and Heptapegon, staying with disciples whom I met in Dedan's house on the first day of the week.

These disciples have confirmed most of the stories which Lydia and Julia told me, and it's clear that thousands of Galileans gathered to listen to Jesus.

They are poor uneducated people, and they loved him. They hung on his words. They say that he cared for them more than their parents. They knew that he was on their side. And they were bitterly disappointed when he refused to lead them in revolt against the Romans.

As Mnason said, he was concerned both with how they ordered their own lives, and with how they were ordered about by the authorities.

One of the leaders among the disciples here in Julias, a man called Hakkoz, seems to have a very retentive memory, so I'm hoping to stay with him for a few days to transcribe his words. Like most of the men around here, he's a fisherman; and an elderly disciple has agreed to take Hakkoz's place on his boat while he talks to me.

When I first met him, Hakkoz summarised Jesus' message to the common people like this: 'Follow me, guard against greed, fear God, don't worry, sell your possessions, give to the poor, always rejoice, and remember that the spirit will help you whenever you're in trouble.'

That's exactly what they do. They follow his example. They live with simplicity. They depend on their God and each other for everything. And they don't collect wealth or possessions.

By the way, Hakkoz has already added to my collection of amusing stories which have a gladiator's thrust at their ending. This one is about a rich man whom Jesus called 'a fool' for trying to become rich on this earth when he knew that one day he'd die and leave all of his wealth behind him.

I wish you could meet these people, Theo. I could easily stay here and live among them as their physician. But I know that I couldn't live with their simplicity in Philippi.

I want to be like them, but deep down I'm afraid that my life would be ruined.

With best wishes,

Luke.

P.S. Nobody's mentioned my horse!

10th February AD59

Tiberias
Lower Galilee
Palaestina

Dear Theophilus,

I thought I'd better write before you start thinking that I've forsaken my research to become a Gennesaret fisherman.

Don't worry! One trip in Hakkoz's boat was enough. He insisted that I accompany him fishing one night, and I thought it rude to refuse him.

I've always mocked Paul's anxiety about sea travel, but that night convinced me I was made for dry land. It was terrifying! Every creak of the timbers convinced me we were sinking!

Take it from me, Theo, there's a vast difference between these craft and the Neapolis trading vessels you know. I'll never travel in a small boat again, and neither will you if you have any sense.

It took me longer to transcribe Hakkoz's memories than I'd expected, and then Dedan called to say he'd remembered some more. But don't think it's been tiresome: I could listen forever.

Back in Philippi I yawned when Lydia read from her manuscripts (please don't tell her), but now the same stories grip me when they come from the lips of the people who heard them in person.

I'm starting to feel that I know him. I can imagine his

rough accent, I know the words he used, I laugh at his stories (even when they hurt), and I rejoice – how I rejoice – when I examine someone he healed.

As you're always saying, we're useless physicians. The people of Philippi trust us with their money and their bodies, but in truth we do little to help them. We've not made the blind see, the lame walk, or the deaf hear. And if we did, our patients would rouse the whole city. Yet I have to drag the details of his miracles out of the people who saw them. Why? Because they treasure his words much more than his wonders.

It's such a contrast to Jerusalem. There I met nothing but mistrust and hostility: yet here by Gennesaret I'm welcomed and feasted (with fish, always with fish)!

Only one thing has disturbed the joy of these weeks. Dedan returned with new stories, and among them was one which cut deep. It was another amusing story about a rich man who ignored a poor man and got his come-uppance after death.

But the point which affected me most was Dedan's insistence that the rich man wore purple. Nobody wears purple in Galilee. I doubt if Dedan has ever seen purple. But you know what I always wore in Philippi.

I only dressed in purple cloth because Lydia sold it to her lodgers so cheaply, yet I feel that when Jesus told this story thirty years ago he meant it for me today.

I can't get the word purple out of my head. Every night my dreams are full of purple people wearing purple clothes: last night I even dreamt I was eating purple fish!

But you know I'm not rich – not like Timon and Arnan – and I don't ignore the poor. So why does this story ring round my mind?

It's as though there's a voice inside me which won't stop whispering 'purple fool', 'purple fool'. I've tried taking an infusion of dill and cummin, but even that didn't make any difference. Perhaps I've just eaten too many fish!

I've learnt all I can from the people of the lakeside, so I'm now off to visit the towns and villages to the south-west of Gennesaret.

Keep well. Write soon. Remind my patients that I'm still alive. And make sure those manuscripts are in Maritima before me.

With best wishes,

Luke.

18th February AD59

Nain
Lower Galilee
Palaestina

Dear Theophilus,

In the last few weeks I've visited every town and village on the west coast of Gennesaret, and every settlement to the south-west of the lake.

Some of the villages must be a thousand years old, but Tiberias (where I last wrote from) is a modern town which was only established forty years ago. I found little trace of Jesus there, in fact his memory is strongest in the small villages: he seems to have preferred them to the towns.

I've been surprised by Galilee. It's not as large as I imagined. The lake is only thirteen miles by eight; and no village is more than three miles from its neighbour. Jesus appears to have spent most of his time in the small area around the northern shore, and to have made occasional journeys from there to the different clusters of villages in Lower Galilee – rather like me.

It takes me almost no time to travel on horseback from one village to the next. So I have to keep on reminding myself that it would have taken him longer by foot. The roads weren't as good then as they are now, and he would have been hampered by the thousands of people who clamoured for his attention.

Yesterday I stabled my horse in Itabyrium and climbed

Mount Tabor – it's by far the most prominent hill in Galilee. It hasn't been mentioned by any of my witnesses, but so many have told me he went into the mountains to pray that I'm sure he must have climbed it. I did some hard thinking on the top.

I'm writing this letter from an inn in Nain, a large town on the southern edge of Galilee where Simon said a dead son returned to life. I hope to establish the truth about the story. If my research is fruitless I'll ride another ten miles south to surprise Simon in Ginae – I'd like to meet him again.

Your loving friend,

Luke.

23rd February AD59   **Nain**
▓▓▓▓▓▓▓▓▓▓▓▓▓▓▓▓▓▓▓▓   **Lower Galilee**
                                                      Palaestina
Dear Theophilus,

It took me several days to find the man Simon mentioned, but I managed in the end. He's almost fifty now, and is convinced that he's destined to live to a hundred!

He was reluctant to talk to me as he's had to put up with so much attention from the townspeople. But eventually he said what he knew, and I've checked his story against the memories of other people who were present. As far as I can make out, this is what occurred.

Jesus arrived at the Nain town gate with a great crowd of disciples just as this man's body was being carried out in an open coffin for burial.

His mother, a widow, was absolutely distraught at the death of her only son. Everyone felt very sorry for her.

Jesus must have realised what was happening because he went up to her and said, 'Stop crying.' Then he walked over to the coffin, leaned into it, and told the corpse to stand up!

The man says that he can remember feeling ill, and the next thing he knew he was sitting up in a coffin surrounded by a crowd of terrified people! This is what he said:

A man whom I'd never seen before was leaning over me, so I asked him, 'Who are you? What's happening?' He didn't say a word. He stared at me for a few seconds with his mouth twitching in a small smile. Then he grabbed me, threw me over his shoulders, marched over to my mother, and half dropped me at her feet.

She fell on me, sobbing and saying my name. I could feel the crowd's silence – they weren't sure whether an outrage or a miracle was happening. But the moment I moved they went wild – screaming praises to God at the top of their voices.

When mother and I got up to thank the man – we realised that it had to be a prophet – he'd gone! We could only see the back of his head bobbing in the distance as he strode into Nain surrounded by hundreds of excited people.

This incident convinced everyone that Jesus was a great prophet, and news of the miracle spread like wildfire across the countryside. The man says that he hardly got any work done for months because of all the people who came to stare and ask what had happened.

Months ago, Theo, when I was still on the boat and hadn't arrived in Palaestina, I wrote to you about a strange event in Troas. I wouldn't say what it was because I was so ashamed of my error. But now I'm beginning to think that maybe something mysterious happened.

I was sitting in a meeting feeling very sleepy when a young man fell three floors to the ground from an open window. I dashed downstairs to examine him, but he was clearly dead – or so I thought. Yet when Paul reached the scene, he took one look at the boy and announced he would live. And with that the boy sat up!

I still don't know whether my diagnosis was faulty or a miracle occurred. Has anything like this happened to you?

We live in strange times, Theo. These Galilean followers

insist they're God's friends; and they do have something about them – a power, an authority, a simplicity – which can only have come from him. It's little wonder that the Pharisees, who are not like this at all, are so opposed to them: they know they're dead men in comparison.

I don't want to spoil the memory of meeting this man by visiting any more places. He's given me too much to think about. Paul wanted me back in Maritima before the end of the month, so I'll surprise him by arriving back early.

Pass on my news to Lydia: with good fortune, Paul will be freed in April and I'll be home by mid-summer.

Yours,

Luke.

8th March AD59
Caesarea Maritima
Samaria
Palaestina

Dear Theophilus,

Many thanks for all the kind letters which were waiting for me at Philip's house. I was disappointed that the manuscripts hadn't arrived, but was relieved that you'd commissioned Flavius to copy them. I know they'll be a great help.

Thanks again for all the news from Philippi about my patients, and for yet more extracts from the *City Journal*. I realised yesterday that I'd been away for almost eleven months, so it's good to be kept in touch with events.

Nothing much has happened here in my absence. Philip says that Antonius Felix has imposed an even stricter regime while he waits for Nero's decision. Apparently he has executed Jews and Syrians at the slightest hint of trouble.

Paul has had several audiences with Felix, and thinks that he's turning against the Jews. (He said to me yesterday that Felix has the power of a king, but the mind of a slave!) If that's right, it must increase Paul's chances of being released next month.

Julia relished my news from Galilee, and made me repeat the new stories until she had memorised them. I pressed her about the purple clothes, and she thought it probable that Jesus did have me in mind when he mentioned the colour: she says such things are commonplace in the Way.

I asked her whether she thought I was rich and unfeeling towards the poor. She gazed at me more tenderly than before, squeezed my shoulder, and told me how much she cared for me. (I grew pleasantly uncomfortable at that!)

Then she let go and said that I did everything for myself – that I even served others to satisfy my own feelings. Julia accused me of leaving my patients because I wanted to travel; of serving Paul because I was curious; of researching the Way for my own education; and of travelling by horseback because I was lazy. She said that I did all the right things for all the wrong reasons, and that God noticed my motives but disregarded my deeds.

She then launched into a passionate description of Jesus and explained how he'd never thought of himself, but only of others. She showed me his perfect generosity and kindness, and reminded me of her father's example in persecution and rioting. I denied all her charges, but she shamed me. She shamed me as I've never been shamed before.

I want to be different. I want to be joyful like the disciples of Galilee. I want to live like the Jesus I'm researching. But I don't want these uneducated people to know they've convinced me. I don't want Paul crowing over another Macedonian convert. I don't want to be sent all over the Empire carrying messages to common disciples. I just want to finish my research and return to my patients.

Theo, my friend, I need something to soothe my troubled mind. Please send me some of your sane words, they always help me so much.

Write soon, and send the letter by the fastest ship possible. And please ask Lydia to pray for me.

With best wishes,

Luke

26 March AD 59.

Dear Theo,

Extraordinary news!
Antonius Felix has had Jonathan
assassinated (he was the Jews' last
High Priest), despite the fact that
Felix owes his position to Jonathan.
The Jews are in uproar, and a
delegation have sailed for Rome
demanding that Nero replace him as
Governor!
Don't know what this means for Paul
and me. As ever, Luke.

Caesarea Maritima, Samaria, Palaestina

POST CARD

His:
The
Phys
Phili
Maed

Dear Theophilus,

Today is the first anniversary of my hasty departure from Philippi. I never thought then that I'd still be in Palaestina in twelve months' time.

I have no reason to celebrate, for the feast of Lamb and Unleavened Bread came and went without the traditional release of prisoners. Felix realised that he dared not inflame the Jews any more.

It's the first time I've known Paul to be depressed – it only lasted two days, but at least it showed that he's human. He began to cheer up when a letter arrived from Aristarchus (he was one of our party on the sea crossing) which reported that many Thessalonicans had joined the Way. Paul was so pleased that he immediately dictated a letter insisting Aristarchus return here to tell him the news in person!

We've also heard from Manaen, that's the leader of the Way in Syria whom Paul wrote to on my behalf. He described Herod Antipas' attitude to Jesus, and reported that Herod had heard about Jesus, had always hoped to meet him, had very much wanted to see him work a miracle, and had been one of the judges who tried Jesus after his arrest in Jerusalem.

Manaen also suggested that I should contact the widow of Herod's steward, Chuza. He says that she caused uproar in the Palace by leaving Chuza to travel with Jesus as a disciple. He's given me her whereabouts: she's now living in a village near Jerusalem.

Things have settled down since my disagreement with Julia last month, but I've stopped attending the meeting on the first day of the week. Julia is making a special effort to be kind to me, and Philip has complimented me on my notes. I think that Paul must have picked up something because he's been uging me to go back to Jerusalem and do some more research.

I suppose I must face reality and admit that I won't be

home by mid-summer. I don't know what to suggest about my patients. Perhaps you should start listing them as your own – you've probably treated some of them more often than I have.

Please keep sending me news, and please encourage Lydia to write more than she does – her letters always cheer me up.

Your loving friend,

Luke.

17th May AD59

Antipatris
Samaria
Palaestina

Dear Theophilus,

Everything has gone wrong with my plans. In fact I became so dejected that I almost gave up on my research.

I had intended to leave for Jerusalem three weeks ago, but the journey was postponed when my horse stumbled in a pot-hole and went lame. That may seem like a small matter to you, yet it drove me into a darkness which I've not known since my days as an apprentice.

I'm not sure what's caused it. It may be the tensions in this city between the Syrians and the Jews, but it's more likely to be my feelings for Julia.

The truth is that I cannot abide her thinking me selfish. You know that I began researching the Way partly to impress her with my learning and knowledge, but now she thinks me self-centred there seems little point in carrying on. I've twice caught myself sitting on the harbour wall as the Miletus boat sails, and have had to prevent myself leaping aboard and leaving this province behind.

Your letter about the Capernaum disciples helped, and your remarks about the man in Nain cheered me no end – you may think that I'm changing, but you should place your latest comments next to your earlier ones about Cleopas! Is it my letters or Lydia's words that have made the difference?

Thank you also for your reassurance about purple. My problem is that you can only compare me with our colleagues in Philippi: you can't contrast me with people like Philip, Dedan, Hakkoz, Mnason and Paul.

Mnason visited me last week with some news, and to ask me to accompany him to First Fruits. I didn't see any of the celebrations last year, and I knew that I could do with a change, so I agreed. I'm in his house, writing to you while he prepares for the journey.

His news came from his home island of Cyprus. Mnason had mentioned my research in a letter, and the reply stated that one of the leaders of the Way there, a man called John Mark, had just completed his own manuscript about Jesus' miraculous service. Mnason wrote straight back asking for a copy.

I told Paul about this news when I was cleansing his eyes: for a few moments there was a terrible silence, and I felt him go as stiff as a corpse. Eventually he owned up to the fact that John Mark had been a companion of his ten years ago. Paul said that John Mark had deserted him and he'd determined never to trust him again.

I told Paul not to be harsh, and said that John Mark had probably changed in the last years. Then I rubbed his head as hard as I could and said that if he, Paul, had improved in the last ten years he must have been unbearable a decade ago. He couldn't protest at my words becaue he was too busy complaining about your poultice!

Paul insists that I stay in Jerusalem after the feast of First Fruits for another two months of research. He's told me to avoid the Pharisees and the leaders of the Way, and to concentrate on ordinary people. He's also instructed me to visit the villages in the Judaean hills – I'm not sure if this is because he's taken note of my findings in Galilee, or because he thinks that the activity will be good for me.

One of Mnason's friends arrived yesterday. He's called

Beri and he'll be travelling with us to Jerusalem. I had to explain to him about my research, so he wanted to read my notes. I must confess that he was impressed by my writings, and said that he'd only one story to add.

It wasn't a pointed story like the others, it was more a series of sayings about people who begin a project without considering whether they can complete it.

Beri said that Jesus asked a great crowd of followers whether a king with an army of ten thousand would advance against an enemy with twenty thousand? Or whether a man who wanted to build a tower would lay the foundations without checking that he had enough money to finish it?

According to Beri, Jesus said this to remind the crowds that none of them could follow him without giving up everything they owned. But you can imagine that it made me think of my research.

If people would mock a man who couldn't finish his tower, how much more would they poke fun at a physician with a half-written report!

So, I'm persevering, Theo. My zeal has gone, but I'm determined to complete what I've begun. I hope that you'll value the report when it's finished, because – if I remember rightly – it was as much your idea as Julia's, in the first place!

I can just muster enough enthusiasm to send you and my patients my best wishes.

Your loving friend,

Luke.

Dear Theophilus,

The festivities here in Jerusalem have greatly lifted my spirits. The celebrations were only meant to last one day, but they went on all week because the grain harvest had been gathered early this year.

The signal for the fun to begin was the moment on the day of First Fruits when the priests waved two loaves and two lambs before God. The crowds took up the festive wave, and everyone's been cheering and waving ever since.

You don't need to understand it to join in; however Beri says that the loaves were to give thanks for the completed grain harvest, and that the lambs were to dedicate the next three months' work of harvesting the olives, grapes and figs.

These Jews certainly know how to celebrate. (I even saw Eleazar enjoying the fun, though I didn't speak to him.) But the feast has a special meaning for Mnason. He and three thousand others became followers of Jesus at this feast twenty-six years ago; so they count it the real beginning of the Way.

Mnason has explained what happened on that day, and I'm starting to realise how important God's spirit must be. Whenever I ask a disciple for a serious explanation about anything, I'm always told that it's down to 'the spirit'. They seem to think that it's impossible for anyone to think and live differently without the help of this spirit. But I've no idea how to receive its help – or even whether it's real.

Mnason and Beri are returning to Antipatris tomorrow, and I'll restart my research by riding to meet Chuza's widow. Tell Lydia that I feel better already!

With best wishes,

Your uplifted friend,

Luke.

Dear Theophilus,

Chuza's widow is called Joanna, and she lives here in Gibeah
– a small village on the main road three-and-a-half miles
north of Jerusalem. I must have ridden past her house without
realising it at least four times in the last year.

I've been sitting in her house with my quill in my hand
for over an hour now, trying to find the right words to
describe her. Whatever I write is bound to be inadequate
because she's one of the loveliest women I've met. She must
be aged sixty, yet she possesses a radiance, a peace and a
serenity which are impossible to put into words.

Joanna seemed surprised to find that almost all of my eye-
witnesses have been men; there was that woman in Taricheae
last January, but her husband did most of the talking. I couldn't
see what was wrong with that. However, when she'd read my
notes, she pointed out that although I'd accurately described
the Jesus men had followed or opposed, women had followed
him in equally large numbers for quite different reasons.

She also remarked that the two people who'd most
attracted me to the Way were women, and suggested that I
should question more ladies in honour of them!

Joanna was part of a group of female disciples which she
insists was as important to Jesus as the famous twelve men.
She maintains that this group of women supported him most
generously of all, and provided all the money which enabled
him to travel and teach without working. She says they
accompanied him from Galilee to Jerusalem, were with him
when he died, and were the first people to realise that he'd
returned from the dead. (Incidentally, she's verified some of
the stories Cleopas told me.)

Joanna insists the real reason why women loved Jesus so
much was that he didn't look down on them or treat them
as possessions (like the Pharisees). Instead he valued them as
friends. She says that he called women to follow him, went

out of his way to show prostitutes he accepted and respected them, and somehow made ancient, gnarled women feel beautiful in his presence. Young mothers liked the joyful way he welcomed them and their children, and all women everywhere were amazed that he taught them like men.

According to Joanna, Jesus astonished everyone by listening to women, answering their questions, and mentioning them in his stories. She described one incident when a woman in the crowd embarrassed everyone by calling out, 'It's a fortunate womb that gave birth to you, and a lucky pair of breasts that fed you.'

He laughed with the crowd, turned and waved at the woman, then called out so everyone could hear, 'You might be right, my love! But I can guarantee that anyone who hears and obeys God's words is much more fortunate than my mother's breasts.'

Joanna thinks that women were one of the main reasons for the hostility between Jesus and the Jewish authorities. She says they were appalled by his female disciples, by his eating with prostitutes, and by his insistence that women were important to God. And she's certain that the way they treated women was one of the main reasons why Jesus was angry with them.

I've also talked with Joanna about Jesus' teaching on money. She's gone through my notes very carefully, and has explained to me why he demanded generosity more than anything else.

Apparently, Jesus thought people were meant to be like their creator, and constantly argued that God was a generous Father. He taught that because God willingly gives everything all people need (including his love and forgiveness), the people he's made in his image should imitate him and willingly give their neighbours everything they need (including love and forgiveness).

Joanna insists that Jesus refused to allow people to follow him unless they were so grateful to God that they wanted to give everything they had in thanksgiving to others. She thinks that this was yet another reason for his bitter disputes with the scribes and Pharisees. They mocked and jeered his teaching about money. And he called them loathsome and untrustworthy because they loved money.

There's one last thing I must tell you. I can only put it bluntly. Joanna calls me a follower. I know it seems ridiculous, but her reasoning is sound.

Whenever I interview a disciple I start by explaining that I'm a companion of Paul who's been commissioned to establish the truth about the events which took place among them. I apologise for not being a follower myself, but make it clear that Philip of Maritima thinks it should be an honest outsider who writes an orderly account of Jesus' teaching. But Joanna interrupted my little set speech. 'Luke,' she said, 'you are a follower.' I disagreed, and carefully explained that I had met many devoted disciples and knew that I wasn't at all like them.

She ignored my answer and simply repeated, 'But you are a follower, Luke.' Then she leant forward in her chair to give extra emphasis to her words. 'You followed him to Palaestina, you followed him to Galilee, you followed him to Jerusalem, and now you've followed him here. You might not have caught up with him. You certainly aren't in step with him. But there's no doubt that you're following him.'

What could I say when she put it like that? And do you know, Theo, her words made me feel quite warm and contented. I'd been struggling, dissatisfied, not sure what to think, unable to sleep without seeing purple, convinced that Jesus would have been displeased with my life. But after Joanna's explanation I feel more rested and peaceful. I'm not sure whether I've been infected with her joy and serenity, or whether I'm genuinely different. Only time will tell.

Don't tell Lydia in case it all goes wrong.

Your friend,

Luke.

Dear Theophilus,

Although Paul instructed me not to question the Pharisees, I couldn't stop myself testing Joanna's theories upon them. Three days ago I returned to Jerusalem and sought out the old men that Eleazar had brought to me.

I thought it prudent to say that I had been impressed by their testimony and wanted to hear more of their stories. I told them that, while travelling in the north, I'd heard the shocking suggestion that Jesus had eaten with prostitutes and travelled with female disciples. That opened their mouths!

Joanna was right. These men were outraged by Jesus' extraordinary kindness to women. Their bitter words and hateful looks were in stark contrast to Joanna's gentle speech. I quickly realised that Jesus was right to value women so highly: why, Joanna's got more sense and insight than Eleazar's companions together.

You should listen to Lydia, Theo. I mean really listen to her. Not just hear what she's saying, but listen with your mind as well as your ears. Take what she says seriously. Value her words as if they came from the mouth of that old Neapolitan herbalist you esteem so highly.

Anyway, when the old men had exhausted themselves by denouncing Jesus and his army of female disciples, I asked them if they'd ever debated with Jesus about money. I said, again, that I'd heard strange stories in the north which were hard to believe and I needed to hear their opinions.

This time their response was different. Instead of bitter aggression there was sarcastic amusement, and instead of venomous words there was wit, and wry laughter.

They joked about 'his crazy ideas'. They mocked his suggestion that 'a tenth is never enough'. They jeered his phrase, 'you can't serve God and money'. And they ridiculed his demand that money should be given directly to the poor. 'They waste it,', they scorned. 'They spend it all on strong drink', they sneered. 'Much better to give it to the Temple authorities so that they can distribute it wisely, and make God's holy place a worthier place for all.'

What they really meant, Theo, was that they wanted to keep as much as possible for themselves and their holy hobby! ! Their talk made me angry. Really angry. More angry than I've been since Ramon whipped his grandmother to within an inch of her life. It's not like me to wish harm on anyone, but I hope these men get their come-uppance from God when they die.

Don't let me be hard-hearted to the poor when I'm back in Philippi. Stop me when I walk past a beggar. Prevent me from spending my money on purple clothes and fine food. And when you grab my arm, whisper 'Eleazar' in my ear. That will be enough.

It's time for me to take Paul's advice and leave these hypocrites behind. I'm off to talk with the common people – that's where Jesus is loved.

With best wishes,

Luke.

11th June AD59   Jerusalem
▬▬▬▬▬▬▬▬▬   Judea
                                                     Palaestina
Dear Theophilus,

I've spent the last week in the worst part of Jerusalem earning my food by working again as a physician. I've cured the sick, comforted the dying, shown beggars which herbs soothe sores, and surprised myself with the discovery that I prefer the poor.

As I've washed the old men I've asked them about the events which took place here a quarter of a century ago. Their dim eyes lit with excitement at the memory!

They described their joy on the day Jesus came to

Jerusalem – they were convinced that he was going to change everything. They remembered his daft prediction that Jerusalem would be destroyed, his burning anger at the traders who worked in the Temple, and his golden words which gave them such hope for the future.

They recalled their shame at the way they gave in to the Jewish authorities, and turned against Jesus when the chief priests charged him with blasphemy. And tears trickled down their dusty cheeks when they told me about his death. One man said they all came home that day, sobbing and beating their breasts.

A few have insisted that he's still alive. Others spoke glowingly of James and the Jerusalem disciples. But most look back to those months so long ago as the one bright spot in their dark lives of misery.

They all think that I must be a disciple because of the way I care for them. But I wish I could do more. I wish I could explain that it isn't all over. That's what I feel, Theo. His life can't have been in vain: all that goodness can't disappear.

If I had Paul's eloquence I'm sure I could convince them that Jesus' words can still change their lives. But my tongue ties itself in a knot whenever I try to speak about the Way. Later on though, when I pick up my quill, I know exactly what I should have said. Yet it's too late then.

What is to become of me, Theo? I've found such joy immersing myself in the service which Jesus commends, but I'm afraid that it's all a delusion which will soon evaporate.

I know that I'll be sad if I return to Philippi in the same state I left: there's an ache inside me which is far beyond my skills of diagnosis and healing.

One of the poor families I treated for toothrot told me about a village in the hills where a relative of Jesus still lives. I'm going to try to find him soon.

Please tell Lydia my news. She'll know what to do.

Your good friend,

Luke.

Dear Theophilus,

Beth-haccherem is four miles west of Jerusalem, high in the Judean hills. It's a bleak place, but it's home to Lebanah, and he's the closest I've managed to come to Jesus' relations.

Lebanah has told me a story which I know from your letters you'll enjoy – even though I'm convinced that you won't believe it!

He's a wrinkled old man of seventy-six and his family is the one commended to me by the man in Jerusalem whose teeth I pulled ten days ago. Like his father before him, Lebanah has worked all his life as a stonemason: his hands are stiff and gnarled from years of hard work.

Let me explain his relationship to Jesus. Lebanah's mother was the sister of a priest called Zechariah, and all the members of that family lived here. Zechariah married a girl called Elizabeth from the village, and she was descended from the Jews' first priest. It's this girl who was related to Jesus – to his mother (Lebanah has told me she's called Mary); so Lebanah's relationship to Jesus is real but remote.

Lebanah was about ten when the events he described took place. By then his uncle was an old man, his aunt was middle-aged, and it was obvious to all that they were unable to have children. Lebanah insists this barrenness was a great mystery in Beth-haccherem because they were good people who carried out all the commands of the law impeccably.

I don't know what his story means, Theo, so I think it's best if I just copy the words I transcribed from Lebanah.

My uncle belonged to the Abijah section of the priesthood, which served in the Temple for two separate weeks in each year.

During one of these weeks there was great excitement in Beth-haccherem, because the people heard that it had fallen by lot to my uncle to enter the Holy Place in the Temple.

(Apparently, Theo, this can only happen once in any priest's lifetime, and most priests never know this honour.)

When my uncle was in the Holy Place he had to supply the altar with fresh incense. His hands were shaking with nerves and honour, when suddenly he became aware of someone standing to the right of the altar.

My uncle looked up, realised it was an angel, and dropped the jar of incense in fear. He thought he was about to die. But the angel spoke to him gently, urging him not to be frightened, and promising that my aunt would soon give birth to a son who must be named John. The angel went on to tell my uncle that the boy would bring him joy and delight, and that he would be great in the sight of God.

(Lebanah must have told this story hundreds of times, Theo, for he recited the words as if he'd been present himself.)

The angel also promised my uncle that his son would be filled with God's spirit while still in the womb, and that he would bring many in Palaestina back to God.

My uncle thought he was dreaming. He rubbed his eyes, glanced nervously round the Holy Place, then whispered to the angel that he and his wife were too old to have children, so how could it possibly happen?

That made the angel furious. He seemed to grow in size, and blazed at my uncle. 'I am Gabriel! I stand in the presence of God! I come to you with words of good news and you do not believe me! For that you will lose the power of speech until after the birth takes place.'

My uncle was petrified. He was shaking so much that he had to hold on to the altar to stop himself falling. He just stood there clutching the altar in terror, opening and closing his mouth like a half-dead fish, until he realised that the angel had gone. Then he tried to speak – and no words came out.

All this took time, and the people in the Temple were wondering why my uncle was taking so long. When he finally came out of the Holy Place looking dazed, they asked him if he was all right. As he could only make signs at them, they thought he was ill. But when he shook his head and made more signs, they realised that he must have had some sort of vision.

Lebanah told me that Zechariah stayed on in Jerusalem for the rest of his week of service before returning home. His silence astonished Beth-haccherem. And their amazement only increased when Elizabeth hid herself in her home for five months. Lebanah says that nobody saw her until the day she walked out of the door with a belly the size of a young camel's hump!

About a month later, Elizabeth's young relative Mary came to stay, and Lebanah says that she helped to care for Elizabeth until the baby was born.

I pressed Lebanah about Mary, asking him when he last met her. He insisted that he hasn't seen her since Jesus' execution, that he didn't know where she was now, but thought that he would have heard if she'd died. I begged him to try and make contact with her for me, and he said that he would. But I think that he only wanted to get on with his story.

In due time Elizabeth gave birth to her son, and this is how Lebanah described the joyful celebrations in Beth-haccherem at the way God had finally lavished his faithful love on the old couple.

Eight days after the birth, everyone came to the boy's circumcision and naming ceremony. All my relatives wanted to call him Zechariah, but my aunt spoke up and insisted that he had to be called John. The men shouted her down, protesting that no one in our family had ever been called that. My aunt persisted, so they fetched my uncle's writing tablet and asked him what he wanted.

Everyone crowded round and watched as he scratched. 'His . . . name . . . is . . . John.'

They were stunned. Then my uncle put down the tablet, stood up, and whispered in a strangled croak, 'John. John. My, my son is John.'

Pandemonium broke out. Elizabeth hugged him. All of the children started shouting and dancing. The baby screamed. The men poured wine. Everyone was talking and asking questions at the same time. Then my uncle stood on a chair and gestured for everyone to sit down and be quiet. He croaked that he had something important to say.

Lebanah insists that Zechariah was filled with God's spirit sometime during the rumpus, and that was what made him say these words. I'm not so sure. I wonder whether he had been rehearsing them all the time he'd been speechless. Anyway, this is what Lebanah says that Zechariah stood up and announced:

'We must all praise the God of Palaestina because he's coming to help us – his people – and set us free. He is keeping his promise to give us a powerful saviour!

'Long ago, he told the prophets that one day he would save us from our enemies and free us from all those who hate us.

'Long ago, he guaranteed to our ancestors that the day would come when he would show us his loving mercy and remember his binding promises.

'Long ago, he swore to our father Abraham that he would rescue us from our enemies and allow us to serve him without fear – so that we could serve him in holiness and goodness. That day is near!'

Lebanah says that Zechariah went over to the priest who had just circumcised John, and picked up the whimpering baby. Then he rocked him in his arms and quietly whispered these words: 'My little child, you will be a prophet of the highest God. You will go before God to prepare a way for him. You will tell our people that they will be saved by having their sins forgiven.'

Lebanah maintains that Zechariah said this several times, each time a little bit louder, before handing the child to his wife. Then he stood up straight, stretched his arms high in the air, and said in the loudest voice he'd managed so far, 'Our God is generous and kind. He is sending the bright dawn of salvation to visit us. He is about to shine from heaven on all who live in the dark shadow of death. God will guide our feet into the way of peace.'

It's an extraordinary story, Theo. But I can't see how it fits into my report of Jesus' teaching – except that this child must surely be the relation whom Jesus stayed with before starting his ministry.

Lebanah says that the events surrounding the birth filled Beth-haccherem with awe and set the whole region talking. Everyone wondered what John would turn out to be.

Well, the child grew up, and then moved away from the village to live in the desert. Lebanah had lost touch with him when suddenly John reappeared and everyone started talking about him again.

Lebanah insists that John went through the whole Jordan valley urging people to change their minds about sinning, to be baptised, and so be forgiven. He went out to listen to him once, and was shocked by what he heard. Apparently people were asking John what they should do, and he was telling them to share their food and clothing with the people they knew who had less than them.

Lebanah says that he overheard John telling some tax collectors not to take a penny more than the legal rate, and ordering some soldiers to be content with their pay. Lebanah shook his old bald head, 'It wouldn't have worked,' he sighed, 'It wouldn't have worked'.

I laughed, because it sounded so like Jesus. Maybe this is where Jesus got some of his ideas!

John didn't live long. He criticised King Herod for his relations with his brother's wife, so Herod locked him in prison and had him beheaded.

I asked Lebanah if he'd ever met Jesus or heard him teach, but he says that Jesus had little time for his relatives. He maintains that Jesus never visited this village, and that he only watched Jesus' execution out of family duty.

I'd hoped to learn the location of Jesus' mother from Lebanah. But even though he's promised to try and contact her, I expect that he'll forget me the moment I ride on. I'm not sure where to turn next in my search. I think that the best thing to do is visit James again. Maybe I can persuade Joanna to write a letter of introduction.

I hope those manuscripts are on their way by now. I can't remember hearing anything in them about Jesus' family, but there might be a small clue somewhere.

Please pass my good wishes on to Lydia, and remind all my patients that I still haven't forgotten them.

Your good friend,

Luke.

26th June AD59   **Gibeah**
▬▬▬▬▬▬▬▬▬   **Judea**
                                                  Palaestina
Dear Theophilus,

As you can see, I'm staying with Joanna while she tries to arrange a meeting with James. She thinks that it would be best if we met him together, so she's invited him to a meal, and we believe that he's coming in five days' time.

I've had several long talks with her about Jesus and the Pharisees, and she insists that I mustn't think all the Pharisees were violently opposed to him. She maintains that some members of the Jerusalem Council secretly supported Jesus, and that a small group of northern Pharisees sympathised with his ideas. That makes sense to me, because Simon of Ginae spoke more warmly of Jesus than Eleazar's companions.

Joanna says that the northern Pharisees asked Jesus serious questions, and she's sure they weren't trying to catch him out. She even thinks that they once tried to warn Jesus when Herod planned to kill him.

She's told me some interesting details about these secret followers – which I've transcribed – and she's helped me to understand Paul rather better. (Have I ever told you that he is a Pharisee? It explains some of his ways!)

Joanna is still treating me as a follower. It's strange. But pleasant. Like the first dose of a new potion.

I'll write again when James has been for a meal.

With best wishes,

Your friend,

Luke.

2nd July AD59

Gibeah
Judea
Palaestina

Dear Theophilus,

James came last night. It was a pleasant enough evening, but oh, so frustrating!

He was polite and kind. He complimented me on my research. He thanked me for caring for Paul. He said that he hoped I'd join the Way. But he wouldn't tell me one word about his childhood.

Whenever I pressed him, he said that it was unfair on the other leaders if he emphasised his kinship with Jesus. He kept on saying that he no longer considered himself his brother – like everyone else he was only his servant. That's nonsense!

Everyone knows he's his brother.

James is clearly embarrassed to have grown up without realising that his elder brother was the promised Messiah, and he still doesn't understand why he refused to believe him when he worked so many miracles.

But the reality is that James refuses to divulge any information about Jesus' childhood, and insists that he knows nothing about his birth.

However, he does admit that his mother is still alive; although he says she's weak and elderly, and it's his duty to protect her from the many people who're always asking to meet her. He says that he has to be constantly on guard in case the Jewish authorities use her to attack the Way.

Joanna asked him gently if he would write to his mother, or visit her, and explain about my report. She suggested he mentions that Paul and Philip are in favour, that he'd met me himself, and that it was important the true meaning of her son's teaching was preserved. Even James couldn't say no to Joanna! He's promised to contact his mother in the near future.

We had a fascinating discussion about wealth, money, hospitality, possessions, the rich and the poor. He agreed with everything I said, and insisted that I had interpreted Jesus' words accurately.

I'm not sure what to do now (I always seem to be writing that to you, Theo); Joanna has advised me to spend more time working as a physician among the poor of Jerusalem, before visiting a town called Jericho: she says that some disciples there may be able to help me. However, I want to see Julia again: I want to find out what she thinks about Joanna calling me a follower.

I'll let you know in my next letter what I decide to do – you can live in suspense for a few weeks!

Best wishes,

Luke.

5 July AD 59.

Dear Theo,

Suspense over! A note
arrived yesterday from Philip saying
that a manuscript had arrived from
Philippi. So I rode here immediately.
You did right to send Quartus'
script when it was completed and
not to wait for Flavius to copy both.
I'm going to stop here until I've
finished working on it.

Many thanks for your help.

Yours, Luke.

POST CARD

His T
The S
Phys
Philip
Maedo

Caesarea Maritima, Samaria, Palaestina

Dear Theophilus,

I've been working on Quartus' manuscript for the last seven weeks. I've zealously compared it with my own, checked all its ideas with Philip and Paul, and am slowly incorporating much of it into my own report. I can't wait to send it to you.

Paul was delighted to see me back almost two weeks early. He insists that his eyes deteriorate when I'm away and only improve when I return to care for them. I'm sure that's due to your poultice and not my skill, for I could tell that he hadn't used it while I was away. (There were too many herbs left in the jar!)

There have been some extraordinary developments here in Maritima. Do you remember me telling you that Antonius Felix had sent the leading troublemakers to Rome for Nero to settle the dispute between the Jews and the Syrians? And that a delegation of Jews had sailed after them to beg the Emperor to replace Felix as Governor? Well, we heard this week that Nero has decided in favour of the Syrian settlers – and has ordered Felix to return to Rome by the end of the year.

The Jews don't know whether to rejoice or to weep. They're furious about the settlers' civil rights, but delighted that they've finally seen off Felix. Mind you, as Paul says, whoever replaces him is likely to be as bad.

I expect that you really want to hear about Julia, and to learn of Paul and Philip's reactions to the idea of me being a follower. The shameful truth, Theo, is that I haven't been able to tell them.

I know that sounds weak, I am weak, but I don't know what to say to them. I don't want Paul crowing about another Macedonian convert, and I don't want to face a long list of questions which are probing for a change in my thinking.

I'm the same Luke who left for Jerusalem three months

ago. I was following him then – just as you're following him now, Theo, by continuing to read my letters. The only change is that I'm prepared to recognise my interest, even my devotion, but I'm not ready to announce it.

I suppose even that's not entirely true. I could tell any stranger that I was a follower. I could admit to any Pharisee (would *like* to admit it, just to annoy them) that I follow Jesus of Nazareth. But I can't tell the people who mean most to me. Why, Theo? Am I too proud? Or am I frightened that they'll laugh at the idea and dismiss it as nonsense?

Your many letters have brought enormous comfort. And it's most interesting to compare your more recent ones with the first few you sent me. But you still want to know 'How?' about everything. 'How did he heal?' 'How did he eat if he gave away everything?' 'How did he return from the dead?' 'How do I know what his words mean?'

Oh, Theo! If you were here you wouldn't ask such questions because the answer is always the same. 'It's God's spirit,' they say, 'God's spirit.' I'd have mocked that myself two years ago, for I never believed Lydia, no matter how hard she urged me. But the proof is the lives of the people I've met, disciples like Dedan, Hakkoz, Julia, Mnason, Joanna and scores more.

They're like they are because they follow Jesus. I want to be like them. So that means I must follow his words and example as well. And maybe, just maybe, God will one day give me his spirit as he's given it to them. They say that's what makes the difference. I know it sounds vague on parchment, but I tell you that it's starting to fill me with joy and peace.

When I've finished with Quartus' manuscript I'm going to ride back to Jerusalem to complete my research there.

Much love to Lydia. Tell her that I'm a follower, and tell all my patients, too. That way I won't have to tell them myself when I return home!

Best wishes,

Luke.

Dear Theophilus,

When I'd finished introducing many of Quartus' words into my report, I rode back here to end my Jerusalem research.

Paul expects Felix to do something about his imprisonment before he leaves for Rome, so he's told me not to be away from Maritima for more than three weeks.

I've concentrated on questioning the older disciples, though few knew Jesus personally, as most of them became followers after his death. One of them, a man called Tiras who was trained as a scribe, has added to my collection of pointed stories.

He asked to see my notes, and when he read one of Quartus' stories it reminded him of two more which were like it. Tiras says that Jesus told them to a group of scribes who were debating with him about eating with sinners. They were outraged by the characters in the stories and by their conclusions.

The first was about a woman who lost some money; and the second was about a man who'd wasted his inheritance on prostitutes and then worked on a pig farm. The gladiator's thrust at the end of both stories was the massive rejoicing which occurred when the woman found her money and the man returned to his father, still smelling of pigs.

But the point for me, Theo, is that these stories have unlocked my unwillingness to tell the Maritima disciples about my following. It's not that I'm proud. (Have you ever met a proud physician? You're always saying that we're useless servants.) It's not that I'm frightened of ridicule. (We're used to that!) It's that I'm embarrassed at the thought of their rejoicing. Paul won't crow; he'll rejoice. Julia may cry, but it'll be her way of expressing joy.

If there's loud rejoicing in heaven when someone changes their mind about sinning, how can this man silence the quiet rejoicing on earth? I know I'll be embarrased by Julia's rejoicing, but I shouldn't deprive her of her moment of happiness.

Does that make sense, Theo? If it doesn't it'll be too late by the time you reply, for I'll be back in Maritima and the rejoicing will be over!

With best wishes,
Your good friend,

Luke.

8th September AD59

Jerusalem
Judea
Palaestina

Dear Theophilus,

Tiras the scribe has been a great help, for his memory is better than Hakkoz's. He has read my packets of parchments more thoroughly than anyone: altering, adding and arrowing the words around.

He confesses that he knows little about Jesus' teaching in Galilee, but he's added to my knowledge of his days in Jerusalem. But he will insist on writing everything himself, on *my* parchments: he won't let me put it into my own words. As soon as I return to Maritima I'll have to rewrite much of it myself; for although his memory is excellent, his scribal style is like the Pharisees' teaching – ridiculous to an educated Greek!

Tiras has explained much about Jesus' death and the events which surrounded it. The more I learn, the sadder I become: betrayed and denied by his closest companions; flogged and killed like a common criminal; mocked and scorned by the crowds that had cheered him; and then such amazing darkness. You've been a physician longer than me, Theo, you'll have seen hundreds of deaths – you know how dreadful they can be. But wait until you read Tiras' description of Jesus' last days: there can never have been a death like this.

Tiras has added three more pointed stories to my collection (I can't believe there can be many more), but I'm too tired to describe them now. You'll have to wait for my report.

I'm riding north to Jericho tomorrow with a letter of introduction from Joanna to the senior tax collector. She says that I'll like him, but the gleam in her eye has made me suspicious.

Best wishes,

Luke.

P.S. I forgot to say I heard four days ago that James has finally written to his mother.

11th September AD59

Jericho
Judea
Palaestina

Dear Theophilus,

No wonder Joanna had a gleam in her eyes when she said these disciples might help me. I think that I've gained more from two days in Jericho than from all my months with Paul. My confusion and dejection seem to have vanished like a rash after a potion.

The person that Joanna wanted me to meet was a spritely old tax collector called Zacchaeus. He's in his mid-sixties, and he's lived in Jericho all his life. He's extraordinarily short, but with a mind so sharp that it more than makes up for what he lacks in inches. His words, his story, his example – they've made everything fall into place for me: I now know what I'm going to do – what I must do.

Zacchaeus says that he became one of Jericho's most senior and wealthy tax collectors when he was aged about thirty: his father died and he inherited all his possessions as well as his official position. Like all tax collectors, Zacchaeus was loathed by the common people and the Jewish authorities, so he was naturally curious when he heard rumours from the other tax collectors about a new prophet in the north who welcomed them, ate with them, and even had one as a close companion.

Zacchaeus told me that he listened to the rumours and longed to meet the new prophet. But it seemed to him that whenever Jesus travelled south from Galilee he followed the shorter Ginae road through Samaria, rather than using the Jordan valley and the dangerous Jericho road which most Jews prefer.

However, Jesus walked into Jericho on his last journey to Jerusalem, and Zacchaeus described that great day so vividly that I wish I could have been there in person. Here's what I transcribed:

> I was sitting at my taxing table when I began to hear the noise of a great crowd of people shouting and singing. I feared there might be a riot, so I locked away the taxes I'd collected that morning and sent a servant to find out what was happening.
>
> He soon came back with the news that the prophet was in town. I quickly put down my quill and my parchments and went out to see him. My servant told me that the people were excited because one of the blind beggars had been healed on the other side of the town.

(I'd read about that incident in Quartus' manuscript, Theo!)

> By this time the crowd was vast. Almost the whole population of the town had gathered to see the prophet. I tried pushing through to the front, but nobody would budge for me.
>
> I began to get hot and frustrated because I thought that I was going to miss my one chance to see him.

You can see how short I am. I can't see over a child's head. I was desperate. I knew that the people would never make way for me – they hated me too much.

Suddenly I had an idea. I dashed past the crowd and ran down the road in the direction they were going. There was a sycamore tree at the far end of the road, and I scrambled up it to get a better view when they passed by. I hid myself among the branches and waited for the prophet to pass underneath.

They were all walking so slowly: talking and laughing as they strolled down the road. Eventually they came near. I could see the group of strangers who were at the centre of the crowd, but I didn't know which one was Jesus. They came closer and closer, until I could pick out their Galilean accents. Then they were walking underneath me. I leaned down to get a good look, and at that moment they stopped and looked up.

I don't know whether I'd made a noise. But if I did I doubt that they heard it above the sound of the crowds. One of them looked straight at me and smiled. Some of the others pointed at me and began to laugh, but the man who was smiling motioned to the others to stop. Suddenly everybody was silent.

The man, I was sure it was the prophet, stared at me intently for a few seconds; then he shouted my name so loud it made everyone jump. 'Zacchaeus!' he yelled. 'I can see you, Zacchaeus. Come on! Climb down. I'm going to stay with you tonight.'

Before you ask, Theo, Zacchaeus says he doesn't know whether Jesus knew his name because he was a prophet, or because the one of the twelve who was a tax collector had recognised him.

Zacchaeus was so excited that he jumped straight down and hugged Jesus joyfully. He explained to me precisely how wonderful it was to be chosen by Jesus after years of being overlooked or rejected or hated. Then he says that the mood of the crowd began to change:

> The people started to shuffle and mutter. Somebody sneered that Jesus couldn't be a prophet if he was talking to me. Others took up the chant. And soon all the people started hurling abuse at Jesus, calling out that he must be a fraud if he didn't know I was a liar, a cheat, a sinner – and worse.
>
> Jesus stood there, looking from the crowd to me and back again. I expected him to say something, to answer them, but he just stood there under that tree, smiling at me.
>
> The crowd began to get really angry. One or two picked up stones. I wanted him to do something to stop them, when I suddenly realised from the look on his face that he was waiting for me to do something. He was expecting me to speak.
>
> I know it sounds strange, but I don't know what came over me. I wanted to please him and heard myself saying that I was going to give half my property to the poor, and that I would repay anyone I'd cheated by four times the amount.
>
> Most of the crowd didn't hear me. So I said it again. Louder. This time a silence started to ripple through the crowd like a breeze through a field of corn. But I was more conscious of Jesus' expression than anything else.

(Zacchaeus' eyes watered, Theo, when he tried to describe it to me. He paused in his story, wiped his eyes, then went on.)

> Jesus grinned at me, turned to the crowds, and shouted so they all could hear, 'Today! Today salvation has come to this man's house.' Then he grabbed my arm,

raised it high, and bellowed, 'I've come to seek and to save people who are lost.'

What a time Zacchaeus had! He feasted Jesus, soaked up his love and words, and then sold his possessions and property in the biggest sale that Jericho had seen. He repaid the people he'd cheated, bought a smaller house with half what remained, then travelled the length of the Jordan valley distributing the balance to the poorest families. He says that it was the most exciting week of his life – and that it earned him many friends!

It's impossible now to imagine that he was ever a cheat, for he's the perfect example in practice of Jesus' advice about money. And he's shown me what I can do.

You know how I've been struggling to explain that I'm a follower. Well, Zacchaeus says that Jesus wants good works not fine words, so if I need to explain that I'm a follower there must be something deficient in me: it should be obvious to all that I'm following his words.

First thing tomorrow morning I'm going to ride to the Antonia fortress in Jerusalem to find Claudius Lysias, the Senior Roman Officer, and return him his horse. I've had free use of this creature for a year and three months, and each time I've entered Jerusalem I've known that I should return it. But the comfort of riding has been too great to give up. Not any longer.

As for you, Theo. Sell all my effects that you've so kindly stored. Pay the storekeeper his fee, and then go to the poor of Philippi and give them the proceeds. Obtain the best price you can, and distribute the balance among the poorest beggars in town. Say it's from you. Give me no credit. After all, this wouldn't have happened if it hadn't been for your advice in the first place.

I wish you could be with me today.

Your devoted friend,

Luke.

P.S. Tell Lydia that she won't be able to sell me any more lengths of her purple cloth!

13th September AD59
Gibeah
Judea
Palaestina

Dear Theophilus,

Zacchaeus was so excited with my plan that he insisted on accompanying me to the Antonia fortress – he said he wanted to see Claudius Lysias' face!

We rode to Jerusalem together, the two of us on the one horse (fortunately for the horse, Zacchaeus is not only little, he's light as well). It was both a sad and a joyful journey. I was sad to be saying farewell to the faithful creature which had served me so well on my travels, but was rejoicing that I was doing the deed which I knew Jesus wanted. I knew I'd caught up with him at last.

You can imagine my discomfort when I walked into Lysias' presence. However, he was ill at ease too, for he thought that I'd come to complain about Paul's long and unjust imprisonment. He laughed and visibly relaxed when I explained that I had only come to return a horse. He thought for a moment, rubbed his cheek, and then told me to keep it as further payment for the help I'd given the authorities after the Maritima riots. You should have seen Zacchaeus, face when he heard that! The decision wasn't what either of us had expected.

I didn't know what to say next. I mumbled my thanks and muttered something about it being important to me to dispose of the horse as part of my religious devotions. Lysias instructed me to sell the horse and give the money to my gods, then dismissed us from his presence.

I left the fortress quite deflated, but still determined to dispose of the animal. I went to the nearby stables and soon managed to sell it. (Zacchaeus negotiated the sale and obtained a much higher price than I would have done.)

I knew what I wanted to do with the proceeds, and walked straight to the part of the town where I'd stayed in June. I had meant to divide the money between those I had cared for, but instead gave it all to the first beggar we met.

He was a poor shrivelled creature, unable to walk, and when he called out for alms in a pitiful voice I could not reject him or give him a pittance. I emptied my purse into his bowl and urged him to tell no one what had happened that day. His eyes and his tears will live with me for ever. Whenever I'm tired of walking I'll remember his face.

Zacchaeus hadn't said much. But when we left the beggar he smiled and said, 'It is good, isn't it?' I nodded, and then he grabbed my elbow, thrust it as high as he could, and shouted to the whole street, 'Today salvation has come to this man!' We both burst out laughing and walked back to the centre of Jerusalem, hardly able to control our mirth.

We sat down on the steps outside the fortress by the Sheep Gate, and Zacchaeus asked me what I was going to do. I explained that I planned to complete my report, care for Paul until his release, and then return to Philippi to carry on working as a herbalist and physician.

He shook his grey head and said that he meant then, that day, that hour. I must have looked puzzled for he went on to explain that he thought I should be baptised. (All the new disciples submit to this rite.) I had no objection, so we walked round the corner to the Sparrow Pool and climbed in.

Theo, from what I've heard Paul say, this is meant to be a solemn occasion. But you should have seen us! Zacchaeus is so short that he couldn't reach up to pour water over my head. I knelt down in the pool, but my head was still too high for his arms. In the end he resorted to throwing water at me. He threw potful after potful at my head as he called out that he baptised me in the name of Jesus the Messiah.

We climbed out of the pool, and embraced. Then he

walked off back towards Jericho leaving a trail of drips behind him, while I walked here to Joanna's, to tell her all that had happened.

I've only been here a few hours as I wanted to write while my memory was fresh. As you can imagine, Joanna was delighted with my news; but she's had the good sense to say little with her lips, and to allow her eyes to speak instead.

I'm going to start walking back to Maritima at dawn tomorrow. But I'll break my journey in Antipatris to speak with Mnason: I can make the excuse of enquiring about the manuscript from Cyprus – and see if he notices any difference.

With best wishes,
Your loving friend,

Luke.

P.S. Please pass on this news to Lydia, and tell her that I know what it's like to be one of the cloths she colours in her dyeing pool!

15 Sept AD.59.

POST CARD

Dear Theo,

Mnason noticed!
And he says he's heard from
Cyprus that John Mark's manuscript
is being copied, and will be sent
to me at Philip's house.
Now for Maritima and the difficult
part. At every thousandth step I'm
going to stop and remind myself not
to deprive them of their rejoicing.
Best wishes.
Luke.

His
The
Ph
Phi
M

Antipatris, Samaria, Palaestina

102

Dear Theophilus,

I don't know where to start in describing the different reactions to my return on foot to the capital.

Julia was the first person to see me, and she must have thought a terrible accident had taken place for she rushed down the street asking if I were all right.

I told her that my legs and feet ached, I was hot and tired, but that otherwise I was fine.

'But your horse, Luke, your horse,' she cried. 'What's happened to your horse?' So instead of her observing a change I had to tell her straight out that I'd sold it and given the money away.

She asked me, 'Why?' and then her voice trailed off and her expression showed that she knew the answer. But instead of crying as I had expected, she merely exclaimed, 'That's wonderful, Luke,' and disappeared indoors to tell everyone that I'd come home a disciple.

At first her sisters didn't know what to say. They mumbled that they were pleased. They tittered when I described Zacchaeus' attempts to baptise me. And the eldest said that it was the happiest day since before her mother had died.

Philip didn't talk. He just sat there with a frown on his face while his daughters fluttered around like a flock of excited sparrows. When they'd exhausted their questions, Philip gravely said he hoped that it wouldn't spoil my report.

He explained that he had hoped the report of Jesus' teaching would be written by an honest outsider. I told him not to worry, and said that my report was almost complete, so it had been written by Luke the outsider. And I promised that Luke the disciple would not add any words of his own in an attempt to convince people. (But he might alter the order to make it more persuasive!)

Finally Philip was convinced, and he visibly relaxed. He

said that he hoped my report would have the same effect on others as it so clearly had on me.

His elder daughters clapped and cheered at that, and said they agreed. But Julia interrupted them, speaking up earnestly, saying she was sure that what I'd written was of great importance and would cause people of many provinces to start following Jesus.

We all teased and mocked her enthusiasm, though I felt warmed by her show of affection. Yet she persisted, insisting that this was not her human hope but an idea which had been given her by God.

The others grew serious and said it was possible. I laughed and said it was nonsense. At which Philip rebuked me and said that no disciple should say such things about words which could have come from God's spirit. With his rebuke ringing in my ears, I retired to my room to rest my feet and sleep.

First thing next morning, I went to cleanse Paul's eyes as usual. He was surprised and delighted to see me back early. He told me his news and made me read him his letters. After a while, he remembered to thank me for returning before the three weeks were completed. That was my chance. I casually informed him that my next trip might take a little longer than expected.

He had to ask why. So I told him that I had sold the horse, had given the money away, and was travelling by foot from now on.

He laughed, Theo. He actually laughed at me. Full in the face. Right before my eyes. I felt his spit on my cheek and his mockery in my heart.

When he saw how offended I was by his laughter he coughed in embarrassment and asked if this outburst of generosity was meant to signify anything. I said that I'd given up everything to follow Jesus and if he laughed at me again I'd give up caring for him as well, and would start serving the really needy instead.

Of course he insisted that he hadn't been laughing at my

generosity, and said that he thought I'd sounded pompous announcing it. That made matters worse, and I asked how I could have shown him without speaking. At that he embraced me and apologised for being insensitive. (It was the first time I'd ever heard him apologise to anyone.) And he said how pleased he was that I'd joined the Way.

Then he said that as soon as he was released, I could be baptised. I had to tell him that I had been, and described what had happened with Zacchaeus. His long face betrayed his disappointment at not baptising me himself, but he pretended to be pleased and gruffly said that it was better when the leaders did little baptising, for it was a task best done by ordinary disciples.

There's still no news about his release. Paul has spoken with Felix, and has asked when he would be leaving for Rome and what will happen to those men in prison who are waiting for judgement. But Paul hasn't heard the Governor's answer. He thinks that Felix is unlikely to set him free now because he's trying to gain favour with the Jews so that they'll send a better report to Nero. However, Paul is convinced that he'll be released as soon as the new Governor arrives. We don't know who it will be or when he is coming.

Two more of your letters have arrived, and the most recent contains your reactions to my report from Lebanah about the birth of Jesus' relation. Thank you for your kind words. As you say, it would be good to include Zechariah's story in the manuscript.

I'm sorry I've not managed to convince you that Jesus returned to life. I promise that I'll try to get more details and will question some soldiers about your suggestions. (I think you must have written before you received my letter about Tiras. That might have made a difference.) I admit that I'm still not clear what happened after his death, and why he disappeared again. I'll try to establish the meaning of those events for you.

Thank you for your wise comments about James. I agree

that it will be helpful to write more about the ordinary disciples than the famous twelve apostles. As you say, everybody already knows their stories. I'm glad that what I've written about Dedan and Hakkoz has inspired your thinking, but I'm sorry you're still asking me not to do anything hasty.

I've hesitated for too long, Theo, and the man whose example shines brighter than all others was one who was rash, impetuous, hasty, and wonderfully unpredictable.

Everybody who met him admits that they never knew what he'd say or do next; that whenever he was asked a question they held their breath, for his answer was bound to be bold and unusual; that he lived on the edge of a stoning because he did things no prophet had done before; and that the stories he told cut straight through their ideas and traditions. Tiras used a wonderful phrase to me, he said that Jesus had 'circumcised his mind'.

So if I'm one of his followers, Theo, I'm bound to become rather more rash and unpredictable than I was when you knew me in Philippi. If, when we've been together for a few months again, you conclude that I'm still the same conservative Luke whose conversation is as predictable as the dawn, then whisper the name 'Tiras' or 'Dedan' or 'Hakkoz' in my ear, and tell me that I'm not like the poor man of Galilee.

By the way, I've had a lovely letter from Lydia, full of kind encouragement and warmth. I've written fully to her describing my change of mind, but please thank her again for her words of comfort.

Pass on my good wishes to all my patients, and tell them that my dispensary will be a more interesting place in the future.

With best wishes,
Your good friend, Luke.

Dear Theophilus,

I've questioned so many soldiers about the way they execute criminals that I'm sure they're suspicious of my intentions! I'm afraid – no I'm not, I'm delighted – that they all think your idea is nonsense. When I've explained that you're a physician, they've said you should know better.

Felix ordered the execution of a Jewish agitator last week, and because of my interest, the centurion on duty invited me to stand with his soldiers and certify the death at the end of the ceremony. The criminal died very slowly.

It's easy to invent a fine theory in a Philippian dispensary, but if you'd seen this execution you'd know that what you suggest is impossible.

Anyway, I've had it on good authority from Tiras, Joanna, Lebanah and Cleopas – who were all present – that Jesus was so weakened by his flogging that he was unable to carry his cross to the place of his execution.

I'm sorry, Theo. You'll have to face facts. He did die. And something quite remarkable happened soon after. How else can you explain the change in all the disciples? How else can you explain the experiences of Cleopas and all the people in Paul's collection of stories? How else can you explain James' extraordinary turnaround? What meaning do you give these events if Jesus did not return to life?

Send me your next theory by the fastest boat possible – before my life is based on a lie. You asked me to establish the truth, Theo. But now that I have you refuse to accept it.

In your latest letter you asked for more information about God's spirit. I haven't any. Nobody has. You must realise that I've asked Paul, Philip, James, Joanna, Mnason, Zacchaeus – in fact just about every disciple I've questioned – for more details about this spirit. But they all shrug their shoulders and insist it's a mystery.

They describe it as an invisible person who comforts and

helps them. They say it's the spirit of Jesus, and of God, and that it's with them all the time. They maintain that it fills their lives like purple dye fills Lydia's cloths – changing and affecting every part. I don't know it myself, but I see its evidence everywhere.

I'm eager to go to Galilee to complete my report, to visit Dedan and Hakkoz again, to walk into that Taricheaen inn on my own two feet, and to try to find Mary – how I long to meet her. But Paul won't let me leave until his situation is clear, so I expect to be here at the end of the year.

I've done all that I can to my report, and had hoped that Lydia's other manuscript would have arrived by now. Why has it taken so long?

Stay well, my friend, and keep thinking about the Way.

With best wishes,

Luke.

P.S. I'm sorry that this letter is abrupt – I'm tired tonight, and not feeling well.

19 Nov. AD 59.

Dear Theo,

Felix surprised everyone by leaving at noon on the Crete boat. He left in this manner to avoid hostile demonstrations which had been planned for the Jews.

After he'd gone, it was announced that a Porcius Festus will take his place, but not until next April. So the province will be without a governor for over four months.

Paul fears that this is a recipe for riots and chaos, and says I can't leave for Galilee until he's safe from the Jews. Still no news from James about his mother!

Best wishes to all, Luke.

POST CARD

His
The S
Phos
Philip
Maed

Caesarea Maritima, Samaria, Palaestina

109

Dear Theophilus,

Paul finally agreed to me revisiting Galilee and completing my research. He was convinced for five long weeks that the absence of a Governor guaranteed the Jews would revolt against the Romans, slaughter the Syrians, or storm the prison to seize him and stone him.

None of these things happened. Felix's sudden departure must have caught the Jews by surprise, and all the regional Senior Roman Officers had been instructed to be vigilant: there are soldiers everywhere.

I'd urged Paul to allow me to leave, and eventually Philip visited him last week and said that I should be allowed to complete my report before Festus arrived, as nobody knew what new laws he'd impose.

Paul's never fully grasped the importance of my research, and now that I'm a disciple he's even more reluctant to lose my companionship and care. Nevertheless, a few days ago he gave his reulctant permission for me to be away for three months. But he insisted that I must return immediately if Festus arrives early.

It only took me a few days to make my preparations, and this time Paul's promised to use your poultice while I'm away. Philip is quite expert in applying it now: I've told him that he could become a qualified herbalist with a little hard work!

Mnason is accompanying me on this journey – he says to tell you that now I'm walking he can manage to keep up. (That's a reference to our progress on the way to First Fruits last year, when I had to keep on stopping for Beri and him to catch up with my horse.)

In truth, I am glad of a companion who speaks both Greek and Aramaic. I have conversed easily everywhere except Galilee, and Mnason will explain to me what people are saying. So this time I won't have to interrupt the people and ask them to speak slowly or use different words.

It's been strange today, following my route of a year ago when so much has happened since I last came this way. The straight new road across the plains seemed endless on foot, and the winding steep pass through the Iron Hills was exhausting. Last year I rode into Capercotnei at noon to rest and water my horse. Today I limped in at dusk needing to recover myself.

I'm going to retrace my last journey and revisit all the people I interviewed then. I want them to know that I'm a disciple; I want them to check my report now that it's almost completed; I want to ask everyone for news about Mary; and I'm hoping to find new witnesses who'll add the final stories to my work.

Best wishes to everybody,

Luke.

P.S. I've still not received Lydia's other manuscript, despite your assurance that it's on its way. Please try and find out what has happened.

11th January AD60

**Taricheae
Lower Galilee
Palaestina**

Dear Theophilus,

We made Diocaesarea at nightfall on the day after my last letter, and rested there for three days while searching for members of the Way in the chief city of this region. But even with Mnason's help, I still found no disciples.

We walked to Nazareth and made further enquiries about Mary, but again sensed hostility towards his family in that place. I would have thought they'd be proud to be linked to his goodness, but they say they're ashamed that a blasphemer grew up in their town. It made me sad, and we only stayed two nights before walking through the hills to Taricheae.

My friend the innkeeper didn't disappoint me. I was grinning from ear to ear when I knocked on his door expecting his laughter. He recognised me immediately. 'I knew you'd be back,' he boomed. Then he glanced around quickly before adding, 'and I knew you'd get rid of that horse. Why! You had disciple written all over your face from the moment I clapped eyes on you.' He went off to fetch his wife, calling out, 'Guess who's here, dear? A walking physician, that's who; a walking physician.'

I introduced Mnason and we have lodged with them for over a week while visiting the towns and villages on the west of Lake Gennesaret. In the evenings, after supper, I've talked with them about Jesus, about the people I've met on my travels, and have explained in some detail why I sold the horse as I did. They understand. But are still too afraid to do likewise.

Last night I tried to explain to them, as Joanna once did to me, that they are followers. I told the innkeeper that he'd followed Jesus by marrying a woman he'd healed; that he'd followed him by remembering his words and his deeds; that he'd followed him by explaining I needed to give my possessions away before I could be a disciple; and then I told him the only problem was that he hadn't caught up with him yet. You know, Theo, he was less jovial and more serious when we broke our fast this morning. I'm sure he's thinking about what I said.

On one visit to Tiberias, we met a group of people who gave me new information. Mnason was asking them for me whether they could remember Jesus speaking about money. One man said he recalled him announcing that the rich had all their home comforts now, but would go hungry in the hereafter. He told me some more of his sayings as well, which I've duly transcribed.

In one of the small fishing villages, a woman remarked that Jesus was always telling her parents not to worry about material things. I found a section I'd copied from Quartus' manuscript and Mnason translated it for her. I was so excited when she recognised it. (Does Lydia know who Quartus is? I'd give anything to meet him, for his manuscript has proved so accurate and helpful.)

Then the woman recalled another occasion when Jesus warned her parents to watch out in case they became so coarsened by the ordinary cares of life that they weren't ready for the day when they'd meet God. He did say such an astonishing mixture of things!

Tomorrow we're going to walk round the lake to Dedan's house in Capernaum and spend some time with him.

Best wishes,

Your good friend,

Luke.

24th January AD60   **Capernaum**
Lower Galilee
Palaestina

Dear Theophilus,

It was wonderful to meet Dedan again, and for a few days I even enjoyed his fish! He was most impressed by my report and congratulated me on my hard work.

I asked him the question I'd been burning to ask since Jericho, why he and the other Galilean disciples had never mentioned my horse nor asked me to sell it.

Dedan explained that it isn't their custom to criticise guests; instead they seek to pass on the teaching of Jesus by living in a way which speaks louder than words. He said that if I had only sold the horse because he had told me to, the Way would be no different from the Pharisees who are always instructing the people to keep every small detail of their religious traditions.

Dedan says that followers of Jesus should live as he lived and give, not out of duty or obligation, but out of love and thanksgiving. Only then will his followers be like their Father in heaven.

I felt so ashamed of my words to the Taricheaen innkeeper (for I'd told him what he must do and had not reminded him of God's love and forgiveness) that I promptly asked Mnason to write him a letter apologising for my foolishness, and urging him to ignore what I'd said and to think only of God's kindness.

On the first day of the week, when the Capernaum disciples gathered to eat and praise God, they asked me to read my report to them. I read what I've written, and Mnason translated my words into Aramaic for the people. It was a moving occasion as some of them heard words which they'd long since forgotten, and others called out that they'd been present when a story was told.

Afterwards, one of the disciples called Gedor solemnly announced that a teaching was missing, and went on to describe how Jesus had taught them to pray. Dedan was highly embarrassed that he'd forgotten to tell me this story, as it took place just after the journey he'd been on with Sheba.

Gedor returned the next day and I transcribed what he said: a prayer Jesus taught, another pointed story (this must be the last), and more sayings to encourage his followers to pray without ceasing.

Gedor's words convinced me that I must pray for God to give me his spirit. I asked Dedan why I'd not felt overwhelmed by the spirit as so many disciples profess. He said that the wind blows with different strengths on different days but that it's always the same wind blowing; and when he's fishing on the lake he values most the breeze which almost passes overlooked.

Dedan said that disciples, like fishermen, remember the rare gale which rocks their boat and reminds them of God's great power, but that on most days God gives his spirit in a gentle way which is almost unnoticed.

I told him, Theo, that his answer did not convince me,

and that I'd only be sure of the breeze after I'd felt the gale.

Dedan smiled in reply, and said, 'Maybe, Luke, but I promise that the breeze blows through you all the time. How do you think you came here?'

I hadn't the courage to say what I thought. 'I rode, I walked, I came, I chose, I planned' – they all sounded too proud and arrogant. Sometimes I think that, despite my Troatian training, I'm an ignorant fool when compared to these uneducated disicples.

Perhaps, Theo, the spirit is blowing these letters your way too. You'd better watch out before you find yourself kneeling in Lydia's dyeing pool!

Mnason and I are going to stay with Hakkoz for a few days soon. (I'm going to ask him to treat Mnason to a night's fishing on the lake – while I sleep soundly!) Then we're going to walk through the towns and villages of Upper Galilee, visiting all the places where I went last year.

With best wishes,
Your friend,

Luke.

Dear Theophilus,

I didn't ride this far north a year ago, but after leaving Rosh-Pinna a few days ago we decided to follow the main road north to visit some disciples in Hazor. (At least I think we decided, we might have been blown!) We then walked north-east across the countryside because Mnason wanted to see Lake Huleh and the marshlands on its northern shore. After visiting them we returned to the hills and walked on here to Kedesh.

If I was blown here it must have been to meet Shavsha,

who's like an unrefined version of Joanna. She's old and wizened, but she treasures her memories of Jesus and tries to live by his words.

We've had a wonderful welcome in her home. Her husband was executed by the Romans for his part in an uprising, and her two sons died of the fever when they were young. Shavsha says that these hardships have made her depend more on God, and that Jesus' words of comfort and hope have been all the medicine she's needed.

I read her my report (Mnason translated as I read – he has been a great help) and the next evening she called in her neighbours and made us read it again. It seems that I'm becoming a travelling teacher on this journey, reading my words wherever I go – it's a very strange feeling!

Shavsha insists that Jesus passed this way, and followed the main road on into the far north. Sadly, we've not enough time to walk there ourselves and research the memories.

Shavsha watched over my shoulder as I rephrased what I'd learnt in Tiberias, and when Mnason explained my words she told me what she remembered Jesus saying – it was all about preparing for a master's return.

When I tried to transcribe her words she protested, maintaining that her memory was not to be trusted. However, I'm so sure we're meant to be with her that I transcribed what she said without her realising. (There are some advantages when the people don't speak Greek!) I'll check her story with the other disciples later on.

Yesterday, when Mnason thanked Shavsha for her meal, she told him not to thank her, for she was simply a useless servant who was only doing her duty. I laughed, and said that she sounded like a physician I knew but, unlike that physician's prescription, her meal was doing some good. (I was thinking of you, Theo, because that's what you always say to your patients when they thank you.)

Anyway, Shavsha put down her cloth, sat down, and grew serious. She said that I was wrong to rebuke her even in jest because she was only obeying Jesus in what she'd just said.

You won't believe this Theo, but Shavsha insists that the very same phrase you use every day in your dispensary is the exact one which is commended by Jesus. She says he taught that we should consider ourselves to be no more than useless servants and should expect neither payment nor thanks.

It seems to me that you must have been a secret disciple all these years and have never had the courage to admit it! You'd better own up to Lydia before my next letter reaches her! What will she say?

With best wishes,

Your loving friend,

Luke.

25th February AD60
Ramah
Upper Galilee
Palaestina

Dear Theophilus,

Paul would be proud of me. I was so encouraged by the warm reception which Shavsha's neighbours gave the public reading of my report, that wherever we've stayed since then I've asked our host to invite his neighbours to hear Mnason translate my words.

I've read it in Merom, Kartan, Yiron, Gischala, Sasa, Horem, Beth-shemesh, Beth-dagon, and now here in the town of Ramah. I tell people that news of the events which took place among them a generation ago have spread throughout the Empire, and that a year ago I came from Macedonia to establish the meaning of the accounts which had been passed on to us. I explain that I've been convinced by the testimony of the Galileans I've met, and now want to remind them of what happened amongst them.

I take care not to say that I hope to convince them, but rather I state that it would help me if they kindly assessed whether my report carries the true meaning of his words.

Deep silence follows our words as old people remember a man that they loved. And then the young ones ply us with questions. I've few answers. (Mnason has more!) I can only repeat his words and urge them to follow him.

Some people have remembered phrases he spoke, and I have added these to my work. I'm now convinced, Theo, that the memory of Jesus will never die out: his words have too much power to guide and change lives. If the one word, 'purple', can begin the change in my thinking which has resulted in our journey through these villages, then surely his other words can convict and bring new thinking to many more people.

For the first time, Theo, I begin to glimpse the possibility Julia mentioned that what I've written for you could be used to help others in Macedonia, and perhaps even in Thrace and Dalmatia as well.

We're going to walk now, reading wherever we go, through the towns and villages I visited in southern Galilee, and then we must return to Maritima before the end of March.

Your loving friend,

Luke.

12th March AD60

Beer
Lower Galilee
Palaestina

Dear Theophilus,
When Mnason and I left Ramah, we followed the road down the Zalmon valley back towards the lake. We stayed overnight at Hukkok with a disciple I met at Dedan's last year, then revisited all the towns and villages along the west coast of Gennesaret. We lodged in a different inn at Taricheae, as I was too embarrassed to face my innkeeper after sending him that letter.

I'd meant to turn west, south of Lakkum on the road to

Mount Tabor, as I had hoped to reclimb that mountain and repeat my experience there last year. But in some way we were drawn south down the Jordan valley and came here to Beer. I think, Theo, I'm beginning to sense that slight breeze which Dedan says is the spirit.

It's many months since I found anyone who was healed by Jesus, but here on the borderlands of Samaria and Galilee I've met someone whose story has thrilled me beyond words. I can hardly control my quill in amazement and delight!

A man, a Samaritan, insists that thirty years ago he was part of a group of ten men who all suffered from a highly infectious skin disease. They were lepers: men who had been cast out by the authorities to live in isolation and poverty. You know what it's like for the lepers in Philippi. It's exactly the same here.

The man told me that they'd heard stories about the new prophet healing people, so when Jesus came this way they went out to meet him. It must have been just a few days before he visited Jericho and met Zacchaeus. He said,

> We were nervous, scared even. None of us would have had the courage to go on our own. We'd meant to go straight up and ask him to heal us, but we were frightened when we saw him surrounded by a crowd of people.
>
> We stopped and just stood there, some distance away, not knowing what to do. Then one of us, I can't remember who, called out, 'Prophet! Take pity on us.' The rest of us took up the shout and attracted his attention by ringing our bells and shouting, 'Have pity on us, have pity on us.'
>
> Everybody stopped talking and turned to stare at us. A man in the middle of the crowd, it had to be the prophet, took a few steps forward. We all tensed in expectancy, hoping, hoping that he would walk up and heal us.

But he didn't. He didn't approach us. He didn't touch us. He didn't even ask us our names. It was as though he was no different from anyone else and scared of our disease. He just peered at us, as people do, and then called out, 'Go to the authorities. Show yourselves to them.' Then he turned his back on us and walked off with the crowd.

We were bitterly disappointed. We turned away, dejected and sullen, our hopes deflated, and started walking down the road. Then one of us, and again I can't remember who said, 'Let's at least do what he said. Come on! Let's visit the priest and see what he says.'

We hadn't got anything to lose, so we headed towards the priest's house, and that was when we noticed the change in each other. We were healed. Every last one of us. Our leprosy was gone. Our hands and feet were normal. Our skin was as smooth and brown as a fresh born baby. Every mark and disfigurement had disappeared.

We ran the last yards to the priest's house and showed ourselves to him – babbling, shouting, crying, almost disbelieving our state. The priest bade us be silent and slowly examined us. We were cured. He said so. Then he fetched his parchments and took an age to scratch the wonderful news that we were free to return to ordinary society.

When we'd been registered by the priest as clean, our first thought was for our families. We wanted them to know the good news, to share in our rejoicing. I said farewell to the others and headed off for my home in Samaria. But I hadn't gone very far when I stopped. I had to speak to the prophet. I had to tell him what had happened. I had to ask him what he'd done. And I knew that he couldn't have got far since we met him.

I chased down the valley after him, and when I finally caught up I was so exhausted that I fell flat on my face at his feet. I lay there in the dust with everyone watching, sobbing my praise to God and my thanks to him. Jesus helped me to my feet and embraced me. He quietly asked me where the other nine were, and whether they'd been healed as well. I answered that they had, and explained that they'd all gone home. He shook his head sadly, then spoke up to the crowd, 'See!' he said. 'Only a foreigner has returned to praise God.'

He looked wistful for a moment, then his face cleared and he smiled at me. 'Go home,' he said. 'You've been saved.'

I've examined the man carefully, Theo, and you would never imagine that he'd suffered from leprosy. In fact I asked him to take me to the authorities to check, and their records plainly showed the severity of his illness.

Theo, Jesus had the power to do the work which we've been trained for. But at depths we've never dreamed of. For ailments we think incurable. And with effects so far reaching that they confound our every idea about healing. He has to be the healer of all mankind that every physician longs for.

The other nine men have never acknowledged or followed Jesus from that day to this, whereas this man has been a devoted follower for thirty years. I've not met any of the nine: I'd like to hear what they had to say!

Mnason and I are going to spend another day here with this man and his family; then we'll visit Nain and try to reach Ginae – I would like to greet Simon again.

Despite asking everywhere, I've found no information about Mary. Nobody knows where she is, or has heard of her in years. Most people thought she was long dead.

There's been no news of Porcius Festus' arrival yet, and I've heard no reports of any unrest in Caesarea Maritima, so I'm hoping to fill every day of my three months with research.

I'm looking forward to reading your letters soon.

With best wishes,

Luke.

Dear Theophilus,

My time in Galilee ended soon after I left Beer. We walked north west across the countryside to En-dor, and from there I was again able to ascend Mount Tabor. I'm sure that Jesus must have stood on its summit, and that some of the events I've described took place on its slopes. Yet I've no proof for my theory so I've not mentioned its name in my report. But whenever I refer to 'a mountain' you must know, Theo, that I'm thinking of Tabor.

When Mnason and I stood on the top of Tabor and looked down over Galilee I felt certain that I'd never come here again. Never walk where he walked. Never talk with the people he taught. Never touch the people he healed or hear again their rough accents.

They're all old now, and in a few years' time they're bound to be dead. It's strange to think that I'm probably the last person to question the eye-witnesses: within a few years people will have to rely on what men like Quartus and I have written. Will they believe us, Theo? Do you believe me? Tell me the truth, I need to know whether these two years have been in vain.

When we descended from Tabor we walked into Nain and were surprised to learn that the man I'd examined had died. Mnason was very disappointed, he'd been looking forward to meeting him. It's odd to think that the man Jesus lifted out of his coffin is now finally buried in the ground. Perhaps he only lived to convince me, for I haven't found anyone who became a disciple through his miraculous return to life.

I read my report in Nain, and Mnason translated again. But my heart wasn't in it so we left the next morning and walked here to Ginae, passing through Ophrah and Jezreel on the way. Just before Ophrah I finally passed out of my beloved Galilee: it was a sad moment and I shed a few tears.

Simon the Pharisee was amazed to see me at his door, for

he thought that I'd long since returned to Philippi. Still, he made us welcome at his table and we've stayed with him for almost a week.

I've told him my own story and I've talked with him about Joanna's theories: he seems much affected. It's difficult for him to think that he could have been wrong for so long, and he finds it almost impossible to believe that Jesus was right about women. I've asked him to visit Joanna when he goes to Jerusalem for Lamb and Unleavened Bread next month, and I pray that her life and her words will convince him.

He read my report with great interest, but I could see that he was troubled by what I'd written. He made no comment when he handed it back, yet last night he asked to borrow it again. I hope he believes – he's been such a great help to my research.

Mnason and I intend to rise early tomorrow and start walking back towards Caesarea Maritima. We'll be travelling through the mountains on a different road this time, on the Valley of Dothan Pass, and will rejoin the new Roman road somewhere on the plains – or so Simon promises.

I'll write again when I've news about Festus.

With best wishes,

Luke.

15th April AD60

Caesarea Maritima
Samaria
Palaestina

Dear Theophilus,

You'll never guess who stepped off the Miletus boat first thing this morning! It was Aristarchus arriving from Thessalonica to give Paul his report!

Nobody was expecting him. Even Paul had forgotten that he'd summoned him. Aristarchus was most perplexed when we asked him what he was doing here. And you should have seen his face when Philip ran to the prison to remind Paul that he'd sent for him – we all collapsed in laughter.

As you can guess, he was amazed to learn my news, and astonished to hear about my report; however, it's good to see him again and hear news from Macedonia.

I was much distressed to read your sad account of the boat which was carrying the copy of the second manuscript, but was pleased that you seemed happy with my news. Thank you for your kind and encouraging words, and for yet more news of my patients.

Festus still hasn't arrived, and nobody knows anything about him.

Philip and his four daughters are well, and Julia sends her special love and greetings.

Your good friend,

Luke.

P.S. Julia says that you won't remember who Aristarchus is. I say that you will. Please let us know who is right.

23 April AD 60.

Dear Theo,

The best possible news!

A trusted messenger arrived today from Jerusalem saying that James' mother had finally agreed to meet me and talk about Jesus. He told me her location, but I'm sworn to secrecy and cannot commit it to parchment.

It's infuriating but Paul says that I mustn't leave until Festus has arrived in case he tries him immediately and I'm needed as a witness. I have never felt so impatient in my life! Pray for me.

Luke.

POST CARD

His ...
The S...
Phys...
Philip...
Maedo...

Caesarea Maritima, Samaria, Palaestina

125

Dear Theophilus,

The new Governor arrived four days ago on the boat from Miletus. Porcius Festus is more elderly than expected, even older than Antonius Felix, and he doesn't appear at all healthy. No sooner had he disembarked than he disappeared into the Palace to recover from the journey. He refused to see any visitors for three days, so Paul was very frustrated.

Yesterday morning he rode out of the Palace and announced that he was leaving for Jerusalem to meet the Jewish leaders. As he said he'd be away for two weeks Paul gave his permission for me to visit Mary — but I had to make a solemn vow to be back within fourteen days.

I've also had to promise James that I won't tell anyone where his mother is living, in case the Pharisees find out and try to harass her. But — here's a clue for you, Theo — I've stopped overnight with Mnason and it should only take me two days of hard walking to reach her from here: I'll be visiting a part of Palaestina which I've not seen before. That should mean something to you and nothing to anyone else!

My excitement redoubled when I arrived at Mnason's house because I found John Mark's manuscript from Cyprus awaiting me. Mnason had assured me that it would be sent to Philip's, but for some reason it had been brought here by mistake.

I've glanced through it. There is little record of Jesus' teaching; yet it describes many stories of his serving which are new to me, and gives details of several miracles which I'd only heard rumoured.

I daren't take the manuscript with me in case it distracts me from preparing my questions for Mary. I'll collect it when I pass this way on my return.

I can't explain the joy and fear which fills me at the thought of my forthcoming meeting. I hope I won't be disappointed by her memories.

I'll write the day after I've met her with all the details of her story.

With best wishes,

Your loving friend,

Luke

A village
Idumea
Palaestina

Dear Theophilus,

If a purpose has been planned for my life then it must have included my meeting this woman. If the spirit exists then it's surely blown me to Mary. And if my report is meant for more people than you and myself, then this woman's sorrow may not be in vain.

Yesterday afternoon, as my footsteps brought me closer to this village, my fear and excitement increased beyond measure. I didn't know what to expect. I dreaded a memory which was too faded to be lucid. I hoped for an example of joy to add to my writings. But I feared, how I feared that she'd be too overcome by her pain at old memories to recount her sad story to me.

I enquired at the edge of the village and was directed to her tiny house. For several minutes I stood in front of her door with my heart beating so loudly that it must have frightened the sparrows. I prayed for calm, and then knocked on her door. A frail, bent old woman opened it and beckoned me in, 'You must be Luke,' she said. 'Come and sit down. I've been expecting you.'

Her weak voice took me back to Galilee, to Dedan and Hakkoz and my Taricheaen innkeeper. It wasn't refined or smooth or educated like Joanna's, but rough and simple and unaffected like Shavsha's. Her hands were hard claws like Lebanah's, calloused and inflamed from seven decades' hard work. She walked slowly, shuffling with difficulty, clearly in

127

pain, grasping the furniture to prevent herself falling.

But her eyes, Theo, her eyes! Though they were old and dim and bloodshot, they shone with strength and peace, they sparkled with joy and praise, they radiated love and contentment. Her eyes drew me to her; without speaking they testified to a greater sorrow than most can bear, and to a greater satisfaction than most will ever know.

Between rasping breaths, Mary explained that she was aged about eighty and had only a few months to live. She said that many people had asked her to describe the stories she treasured, but that they'd always been too precious to share. She reported that James had mentioned my request many months earlier, but that she'd rejected it like all of the others.

However, she added, a dream had convinced her that death was near, and she now wanted to pass on to others the true meaning of the events she had experienced, so that people would not be tempted to invent a false story.

Mary explained that she hadn't the time to tell me everything which had taken place at the birth of her first son, only those things which were important. Suddenly, a dry cough rattled her body and left her breathless. She said that she was too weak to talk any more and asked if she could tell me her story next morning. I willingly agreed, as I was tired from my journey; but I tell you, Theo, such a sense of responsibility and awe overcame me that I slept not a wink last night.

This morning, after we'd broken our fast and washed, she told me to gather my parchments and begin transcribing her words. She seemed stronger, as though an infusion had given her strength, but even so she asked me not to interrupt her or ask questions.

This is the story she told me. There's much to it, Theo. But every word is worth reading. I suspect that it's inscribed on my mind for ever.

Over sixty-five years ago, an angel who stands in the presence of God was sent to visit a young girl in Nazareth. Her name was Mary, and she was engaged to a man called Joseph who was descended from King David.

I was that girl, and the angel came to me and told me, 'Rejoice, child! God is with you. You enjoy his favour.'

These words deeply troubled me, for I was too young to know what they meant. But the angel reassured me, 'Do not be afraid,' he said. 'You have won God's favour. You will become pregnant and give birth to a son, and you must call him Jesus. He will be great. He will be called the Son of the Highest God, and God will make him a king like his ancestor David. He will be king of Jacob's descendants for ever, and will never stop reigning.'

I questioned the angel. 'How can this happen,' I asked, 'when I'm still a virgin?' 'The spirit will come on you,' he answered, 'and God's power will cover you like a shadow. This will make the child holy and he will be called "The Son".'

The angel reminded me of my relation Elizabeth whom we used to call barren. My family had only just heard the news that she was pregnant. 'Remember Elizabeth,' the angel said. 'Even though she is very old she has conceived a son and is now six months pregnant. Be sure of this, Mary: there is nothing that God cannot do.'

His speech convinced me, and I told him that I was God's servant. 'May it happen exactly as you've described,' I said. And when the angel heard this, he vanished.

I was so young. I didn't know what to do. I wasn't sure whether to remain silent or to describe what had happened to my parents.

But before I could say anything, my mother asked me to travel south and care for our relation Elizabeth. I was convinced God had planned that as well, so I got ready and hurried as quickly as I could to the Judean hills.

I went straight to Zechariah's house and greeted my relatives. Elizabeth was heavy with child, and as we embraced we both felt her baby jump inside her – it was as though it recognised my voice.

Right at that moment, Elizabeth was filled with the spirit. She exclaimed loudly, and cried out my name. 'Mary!' she said. 'Mary, you must be the most fortunate woman alive, and your child, too. Why should I be honoured with a visit from the mother of my king?'

Elizabeth stopped and stepped back from me when she realised what she was saying. She was astonished by her own words. She looked me up and down, and her eyes noticed the swell in my breasts. She looked confused, but after a moment she carried on speaking, though more hesitantly. 'You saw what happened. As soon as I heard your voice my baby jumped for joy. How delighted you must be to believe that God's message to you will come true.'

We walked into her room and sat down, clutching each others' hands. Then I spoke with a young girl's rush of enthusiasm. Like Elizabeth, I didn't really know what I was saying, but I can still remember my words. I often think about them now.

I held her hands tight. And while I gazed into her eyes these words came to me. From nowhere. I spoke them slowly, growing in confidence with each phrase. 'My heart praises God. My spirit rejoices because God is my Saviour. He has remembered me, his lowly servant. God has done such great things for me that from now on people will call me fortunate.

'His name is holy. His generous love goes on from

one generation to another for all those who fear him. He has used his powerful arm to scatter the proud and arrogant. He has pulled princes off their thrones and lifted up the lowly. He has filled the hungry with good things and sent the rich away empty-handed. He has kept his promise to come to the help of his servants in Palaestina. He has remembered to show mercy to Abraham's descendants for ever.'

Mary told me, Theo, that she stayed with Elizabeth for about three months before returning to Nazareth when the baby was born. She says that Augustus was Emperor then, and that he ordered several censuses throughout the Empire. At one of the first of these, before the big one which was conducted when Quirinius was Governor of Syria, every man had to register in his own home town.

Joseph was descended from David, so he had to leave Nazareth and go to Beth-lehem, where David had been born. Mary travelled with him, and while they were in Beth-lehem the time came for her baby to be born. She told me how she gave birth to her son, wrapped him in strips of cloth, and – because there was no room for them in the living-space at their lodgings – laid him in an animal's feeding trough.

Mary went on to tell me about some shepherds who saw an angel while they were spending the night keeping guard over their sheep. Although I had promised not to interrupt her, I could not keep still. I put down my quill and started hunting through my packet of parchments.

She saw my excitement and asked me what the matter was. So I told her what I knew and showed her my notes. Even though she could not read the words she was delighted with what I said. She shook her head and smiled at me. 'God has sent you, Luke,' she said. 'God has sent you.'

Then, with an effort, she carried on with her story.

God's glory shone brightly over the shepherds when the angel appeared. They were terrified. But the angel said, 'Don't be afraid, you have nothing to fear. I've come with good news which will bring great joy to everyone. Today, here in Beth-lehem, your Saviour has been born. He is the Christ! He is the promised Messiah! And this is how you will know him: you will find him wrapped in strips of cloth and lying in an animal's feeding trough.'

Suddenly a great army of angels appeared in the sky. They praised God with these words, 'Glory to God in the highest heaven, and peace on earth for all those he favours.'

When the angels had returned to heaven the shepherds said to each other, 'Let's go to Beth-lehem and see what's happened.' So they hurried down from the hills and found us.

When they saw my baby lying in the trough, they told us what the angel had said. Then they went away rejoicing, praising God for all they'd seen because it was exactly as they'd been told by the angel. Joseph and I were astonished by their words, but I made sure that I memorised them. In the years that followed I often thought deeply about them.

On the eighth day, when my baby was circumcised, he was named Jesus – the name which the angel had given before his conception. And when the day came for me to be purified, as our law commands, Joseph and I took our son to Jerusalem to present him to God. This was to observe our law which demands that every first-born male must be dedicated to God. But we could only afford to offer the poorest sacrifice of two young pigeons.

While we were in the Temple, an old man came up to us and started talking to us. He was called Simeon, and he lived in Jerusalem. He was a good and devout man who was waiting for Palaestina to be saved. The spirit rested on him and had revealed to him that he would not die until he had seen the promised Messiah.

This man was guided by the spirit to go to the Temple when we were there, and when he met us he took my child in his arms and thanked God, saying, 'Master, you have kept your promise, so now you can let your servant die in peace. My eyes have seen the salvation which you have prepared in the presence of all nations.'

He handed the baby back to me, and added, 'He is a light which will reveal God's will to non-Jews and will bring glory to the people of Palaestina.'

Joseph and I were amazed by Simeon's words. He prayed for us, and then quietly said to me, 'Your child is chosen for the rise and fall of many in Palaestina. He will be a sign which men will oppose and which will reveal their secret thoughts.'

He paused, then whispered to me, 'Sorrow will pierce your heart like a sharp sword.'

That was a hard saying, which seemed unlikely to a young girl holding her first child. But, like everything else, it has come true.

Mary paused for a while – her eyes showed that she was reliving her memories. Then, with a shudder, she sat up straighter and carried on.

There was also a very old prophetess in Jerusalem called Anna. She was eighty-four years old, a widow, and the daughter of Phanuel of the tribe of Asher. She never left the Temple, and served God day and night with fasting and prayer.

She happened to come by just as Simeon was speaking. She stopped and listened to him, and was startled and excited by what he said. So much so, that this old woman started to praise God and went off spreading the news about the child to everyone she knew who was waiting for God to set Jerusalem free.

That's it, Theo. It took me so long to write this all down that my arm is aching and I've ruined two quills!

It's an extraordinary story to read. But it's been even more moving to hear it from the cracked lips of Mary, knowing that she's describing what happened to her. Her eyes glowed when she described his birth: there were depths of joy and pain that I've not seen before.

Mary has said that I can spend three more days with her to question her about the events of the birth and to verify the rest of my writings. I'll try not to tire her, and to care for her with all my skill. I want to tend her with herbs and soothing ointments; but I know that I've been blown here to transcribe her words, not to heal her wounds. I'll write again before I leave for Maritima.

With best wishes,
Your loving friend,

Luke

23rd May AD60

Avillage
Idumea
Palaestina

Dear Theophilus,
These last three days have been the greatest days of my life. Envy me, Theo. Envy me as you've never envied another before! I must be the most fortunate person in the Empire, to have heard the words this woman has spoken.

I thought that all the cruelty and violence of Palaestina had deadened my reactions, but Mary's loving words and gentle ways have moved me to weep as she's described the sorrows and joys of her life. Everything has been taken away from her.

She described how her child grew to maturity, was filled with wisdom, and was favoured by God. She's told me much from his youth which she's asked me not to repeat, stories which I'm sure she can have told no one before – it's as though she must relieve herself of a burden by telling them before she dies.

However, there's just one event which I begged her to permit me to pass on. Each year, she and her husband used to go to Jerusalem to celebrate Lamb and Unleavened Bread, and they went up as usual when Jesus was twelve. They set off home after the feast, but the boy stayed behind in Jerusalem without them knowing.

They thought he was with others in their group from Nazareth, and it was only after a full day's journey that they noticed he was missing. They looked for him among their friends and relations, and when they still couldn't find him, they walked back to Jerusalem and searched for him everywhere.

It was three days before they found him in the last place they looked. He was in the Temple, sitting listening to the Jewish teachers, and asking them such questions that they were amazed at his intelligence. Mary and Joseph were relieved, furious, and astonished when they saw him.

Mary remembered saying, 'Son, why have you done this to us? Your father and I have been terribly worried trying to find you.' But she says that Jesus just gave them a perplexed look and replied, 'Why were you looking for me? Didn't you know that I had to be in my Father's house?'

Mary told me that she and Joseph didn't understand what he meant; but despite this, Jesus went back with them to Nazareth and lived under their authority.

Mary says that she has stored all these stories in her heart, like jewels in a chest, and has often taken them out one by one to examine and remember them. Throughout his childhood she watched Jesus grow up in body and mind, slowly gaining favour with God and with people.

She recited her family tree, and I've committed it to parchment. She listened to those parts of my report which

I can render in Aramaic, and suggested some changes. She described her sadness when Jesus left home to start teaching, and the stabbing grief she felt when the people of Nazareth – her lifelong friends and neighbours – attempted to kill him.

She said that her other children went with her once to look for Jesus when he was teaching nearby. They could not get close to him because of the crowd, so they passed a message asking to see him. She was deeply pained when he refused to greet them; and says that James turned his back on his brother from that moment, until the day he met him after Jesus' return to life.

She's told me many other things which I've not heard elsewhere, and I'm not sure whether to include them in my report. (She says that I've written enough and should leave it unchanged.)

She wept quietly, and her frail shoulders shook with grief, when I falteringly translated my report of his trial and death. No tears flowed from her eyes: it was as though she'd been drained dry of tears many years ago. Instead, she stretched out her stiff fingers, gripped my arms, and rocked with pain and sadness as she returned in her mind to the torment and sorrow which pierced her soul at that time.

I don't like to leave her, Theo, for she needs a physician; but a better one than me. She needs the healer of all humanity whom she gave birth to. My visit has rekindled her sadness. I want to stay and care for her, but she says that it's time for me to leave.

She held both my hands not two hours ago, gazed deeply into my eyes, and thanked me for coming. She praised God for sending me to write her son's story, placed her calloused hands on my head, and asked God to guide and protect me. Her rough voice crackled with passion and urgency as she went on to ask her own precious son to send his spirit upon me, and to help me write words which would bring his salvation to people of all provinces and throughout all generations.

I couldn't look away as she prayed. My eyes were locked

to hers, and I knew, Theo, I knew that her prayers would be answered. I knew that what I'd written would not be in vain. I knew that God's spirit was blowing through my body (gently, there's still no gale!). I knew that I would never see her again, that perhaps no-one would see her again. And I knew that, somehow, she was passing to me her twin burdens of joy and of pain. I can't explain it, Theo, I can only say that I knew these things better than I know you.

Mary seemed to have aged when she finally stopped praying. She just had enough breath to whisper, 'You must return to your Paul now, he needs you.'

So I'm writing by the light of one of Mnason's best candles, and will be leaving at dawn when I've rested. This journey is over. A new one is about to begin. I don't know where I am going, but I know that I'm no longer alone, for the spirit is with me.

Oh, Theo, please follow Mary's son. Please share the depths of his sorrow and the heights of his love. Please accept the forgiveness he offers and the freedom he brings. Please give with his generosity and live with his life.

Join me, Theo. Join Mary and Julia and Dedan and Tiras and Zacchaeus. Join Jesus. Join his Way. Follow him, Theo. Follow him and be filled with his wonderful love.

Oh, his love, Theo! Like all true love it brings great joy and sharp pain. Yet this is the Way, Theo. There is no other.

With all my love,
Your devoted friend,

Luke

26th May AD60

Antipatris
Samaria
Palaestina

Dear Theophilus,
When I arrived here an hour ago to collect John Mark's manuscript, Mnason informed me that Porcius Festus had

returned early from Jerusalem, accompanied by the Jewish authorities.

Apparently, Festus heard the charges against Paul on the day after he returned, and realised it was a religious dispute. Mnason says that Festus was so anxious to gain favour with the Jews that he disclaimed jurisdiction and urged Paul to agree to be tried by the Jerusalem Council.

Paul refused. He did the only thing he could to escape a corrupt Jewish trial: he appealed to Nero. So Festus has said that he must go to Rome.

Instead of sleeping here I'm going to march through the night to Maritima. Paul needs me, and I fear this means I may not return to Philippi.

It's the first time in months that I've wished for my horse!

Yours,

Luke

8th June AD60

Caesarea Maritima
Samaria
Palaestina

Dear Theophilus,

I reached Philip's at dawn twelve days ago and learnt the full story. It seems that Festus was put under pressure by the Jewish authorities to transfer Paul to Jerusalem only because they were planning an ambush to murder him. Festus came back after eight or nine days, ten at the most, and thought that he could earn their goodwill by forcing Paul to accept a Jewish trial. Like Felix before him he misjudged Paul. So now Paul must travel to Rome in chains.

A week ago King Agrippa II and his sister Bernice (though most insist that she's more than a sister, for they behave like husband and wife!) arrived to pay their respects to Festus. Festus told them about Paul and, because Agrippa asked to meet him, a special hearing was arranged for the following day.

Festus turned the hearing into a circus by inviting all the

city notables and Roman officers into his audience chamber. I managed to gain permission for both Aristarchus and myself to attend as we were witnesses to the original charge.

Festus began by telling the assembly that whole Jewish community, both in Jerusalem and in Maritima, had petitioned him about Paul and loudly demanded his death. He admitted he could find no crime that warranted death and, as Paul had appealed to Nero, he was unsure what charge to make when he sent him to Rome. Agrippa gave permission for Paul to speak, and I thought he spoke as well as I'd heard him.

Paul wisely began by flattering Agrippa. Then he explained that he lived as a Pharisee; told the story of the vision which caused him to start serving Jesus; and said that he declared only what the prophets and Moses had foretold – that the Messiah would suffer, return from the dead, and provide light for all nations.

Festus couldn't stand another of Paul's lectures. He raised his hand and stood up. 'You're going mad, Paul!' he shouted. Paul politely denied this and asked Agrippa if he believed in the prophets. Agrippa didn't answer the question, instead he said that if Paul went on talking much longer Paul would turn him into a 'Christian'. (That's the foolish name which some of the educated Jews have started using to mock and belittle the uneducated members of the Way). With that observation, Agrippa rose to his feet, and the hearing was over.

I heard this morning that we're to sail tomorrow for Rome in the care of a centurion called Julius who serves with the Augustan cohort. The only good news is that Aristarchus has been given permission to accompany us.

Philip and his daughters are greatly saddened by our sudden departure, and I can hardly bear to look at Julia for the distress I feel at leaving her.

In the little time that I've had I've hastily added some of John Mark's words into my report. But I've not had time to work on the information which Mary gave me. As ever, Paul is greatly troubled at the prospect of a long sea journey and has urged me to send my report to you by a separate boat. He says that all my hard work could be lost overboard if it is carried on the same vessel as him.

So, Theo, here's my report, the fruit of my research from these two years. I'm sending you John Mark's manuscript as well, and have marked three sections from it which I mean to add to my own; I've not had time to do this myself, so please will you do it for me? I also ask that you help me to shape a new beginning to my report: please weave together the stories I sent you from Lebanah and Mary and place them near the beginning. I've also enclosed the family tree I transcribed for you to place where I've suggested.

When you've done all this, would you kindly commission Flavius to make two copies of the revised report. Send one to me in Rome (Lydia will know the best disciple to send it to) so that I can thoroughly revise and improve it, before making it more widely available. And please send the other copy here to Philip's: I know that Julia will value it. By the way, I'm taking Quartus' manuscript with me to Rome, I want to use it in my next revision.

So now my good friend, you'd better tell my patients – if any of them still think of themselves as my patients – to sign on your list for ever. For if Paul's foreboding is right it will be many long years before I return to Philippi.

Thank you for your invaluable help and advice. Please go on reading my writings and listening to what Lydia says. I long to hear that you've caught up with Jesus!

Please give Lydia my love and best wishes. I'll write again from the next port.

Your loving friend,

Luke

P.S. I think Paul must have been impressed with my report, for he's asked me to start writing a history of the Way from Jesus' death until the present day. I'll dedicate that report to you as well, and I'll send you a copy as soon as it's ready.

A carefully
researched report
of the teachings of
Jesus of Nazareth

to be assembled by you;
copied by Flavius;
edited, revised and rewritten again by me;
and then made available to people
of all nations.

Please take great care Theo—
This is my only copy!

His Excellency
The Senior Public Physician,
Philippi,
Macedonia

Dear Theophilus,

Many people have written about the events which took place in Palaestina almost thirty years ago, just as many messengers have come to Macedonia to tell us about them. I've carefully researched the story from the beginning, and have written you an orderly account so that you'll know whether the information you've already received is reliable.

(Theo, please place here all the facts in the letters I sent you which describe my meetings with Lebanah and Mary. When I get Flavius' copy in Rome, I'll rewrite the report and integrate them fully. There are several ideas in the report which I want to introduce in Mary's material.)

INTRODUCTION

In the fifteenth year of Emperor Tiberius' reign, Pontius Pilate was Governor of Judea and Samaria, Herod Antipas was ruler of Galilee, his brother Philip was ruler of Iturea and Trachonitis, Lysanias was ruler of Abilene, and Annas and Caiaphas were the Jewish High Priests. At that time God spoke to John, the son of Zechariah and Elizabeth, when he was living in the desert.

Jesus' relative

John travelled the length of the Jordan Valley, urging people to change their minds about sinning, to be baptised, and so be forgiven by God. This is what is written in prophet Isaiah's scroll:

Someone is shouting these words in the desert:
'Get the road ready for God,
make a straight path for him,
fill in the valleys,
flatten the mountains and hills,
make the winding roads straight
and the rough roads smooth.
All people will see the salvation of God.'

So John said to the crowds who came to be baptised, 'You snakes! Who warned you to flee from the fast approaching punishment? Straighten out your lives for God, and do the deeds which show that you've changed your mind about sinning.

'It's useless you thinking that God won't punish you just because Abraham's your ancestor, for I'm telling you that God can turn these stones into children for Abraham! God's axe is raised, ready to chop down trees at their roots, and every tree that doesn't produce good fruit will be cut down and thrown on his fire!'

The people asked John, 'What should we do?' He replied, 'Anyone with two coats must give one to somebody who hasn't got one, and anyone with food must share it.'

Some tax collectors came to be baptised, and they asked, 'Teacher, what should we do?' He said, 'Don't collect more than the legal rate.'

And some soldiers asked him, 'What about us? What should we do?' John told then, 'Never take money by force or false accusation; instead, be content with your pay.'

Jesus and John

The people's hopes rose, and they wondered whether John was the Christ, the promised Messiah.

So John made it plain. 'I baptise with water, but someone is coming who is much more powerful than me, and I'm not fit to untie his sandals. He will baptise you with the spirit and fire. He will have his shovel in his hands to fill his barn with wheat, but he'll burn the husks in a fire that never goes out.'

John told this news to the people in many different ways, but he criticised Herod for all his crimes and, in particular, for his relationship with his brother's wife Herodias.

When all the people had been baptised, Jesus came to John and he was baptised. After his baptism he prayed, and the spirit came down on to him like a dove.

A voice spoke from heaven, 'You are the Son, my Son, and I am pleased with you.'

(*Theo, please place my transcription of Jesus' family tree here.*)

Jesus and the devil

Jesus returned from the Jordan full of the spirit, and was led by the spirit into the desert, where he was tested by the devil for forty days. He ate nothing during that time, so by the end he was hungry.

Then the devil said to him, 'If you really are God's Son, tell this stone to turn into bread.' But Jesus answered, 'Scripture says, "Human beings don't live only on bread." '

Then the devil took him up a high mountain and showed him in one moment of time all the great kingdoms of the world, and said to him, 'I'll give you all this power and wealth, for it's been handed to me and I can give it to anyone I choose. Bow before me and it will all be yours.' But Jesus replied, 'Scripture says, "Bow before God! And only serve him." '

Then the devil led Jesus to Jerusalem, to the highest point of the Temple, and said, 'If you are the Son, throw yourself down; for Scripture says, "God will send his angels to take care of you." And it also says, "They will carry you in their arms in case you trip on a stone." ' But Jesus retorted,

'Scripture says, "Don't test God!" '

Once the devil had finished testing Jesus in every possible way, he left him and waited for a better opportunity.

JESUS' TEACHINGS IN GALILEE

With the power of the spirit in him, Jesus returned to Galilee. News about him quickly spread through the country villages. He taught in the synagogues and everyone praised him.

Jesus in Nazareth

He came to Nazareth, where he'd been brought up, and went to the synagogue on the Sabbath as usual. He stood up to read, and was handed prophet Isaiah's scroll. He unrolled it, and found the place where it's written,

> The spirit of God is upon me,
> for he has chosen me to bring good news to the poor.
> He has sent me to give prisoners their freedom
> and blind people their sight.
> He has chosen me to free the oppressed,
> and to announce that the year has arrived when God
> will save his people.'

Jesus rolled up the scroll, handed it back, and sat down. Every eye in the synagogue was fixed on him. Then he began to speak. 'While you were all listening, these words were coming true.'

They were impressed and surprised by his eloquent words. 'Isn't he Joseph's son?' they said.

But Jesus replied, 'I'm sure that you'll quote me the proverb which says, "Physician, heal yourself," and that you'll tell me to do in my home town what I've done in Capernaum.

'In truth I tell you, no prophet is ever welcomed in his own town. There were many widows in Palaestina in prophet Elijah's day, when there was no rain for three-and-a-half years and a severe famine throughout the land. But Elijah wasn't sent to one of these ! He was sent to a widow of Zarapheth in Sidonia.

'And there were many lepers in Palaestina in prophet Elisha's time, but only Naaman the Syrian was cured.'

Everyone in the synagogue was enraged when they heard this. They leapt up and dragged Jesus out of the town. They took him to the top of the hill on which their town was built and meant to throw him off the cliff. But he walked through the middle of the crowd and went away to Capernaum.

(Theo, please place here the section in John Mark's manuscript which goes from the first star I've marked in the margin to the second. It describes some of the amazing things that Jesus did in Galilee much better than my notes. I hope Mark won't mind! Once again, I'll revise and rewrite this in Rome so that the final report is in the most persuasive order.)

Jesus' teachings to his disciples

Jesus looked at his disciples and said, 'How fortunate are you if you're poor, for God's kingdom is yours. How fortunate are you if you're hungry, for you will be filled. How fortunate for those of you who are weeping, for you will soon be laughing.

'How fortunate you are when people hate you, reject you, abuse you, and call you a criminal because of your friendship with me. The ancestors of the people did exactly the same things to the prophets, so dance for joy and be glad when that happens – because you will be greatly rewarded in heaven.

'But how terrible for you if you're rich, for you're having your fill now. How terrible for you if you have plenty to eat now, for you'll go hungry. How terrible for you if you laugh now, for you will mourn and weep. And how terrible for you all when people speak well of you, for that's how people treated the false prophets!

'I say this to everybody who'll listen: love your enemies; do good to people who hate you; think kind thoughts about people who curse you, and pray for those who ill-treat you. If someone hits you on one cheek, offer them your other one, too. And if anyone takes your coat, offer them your shirt as well.

'Give to everyone who asks you for something, and don't ask for your property back when somebody borrows it. Treat other people exactly as you'd like them to treat you.

'Why should you be rewarded if you love people who love you? Even sinners do that. Why should you be rewarded if you do good to people who do good to you? Sinners do that as well. And why should you be rewarded if you lend to people who you expect will pay you back? Even sinners lend to each other to get back the same amount.

'No! Love your enemies. Do good to them. Lend without any hope of being repaid. Then you will have a great reward in heaven, and will be children of the Highest God. For he is good to the ungrateful and wicked.

'Be compassionate in exactly the same way as your Father is compassionate. Don't judge others, and you won't be judged yourself. Don't condemn other people, and you won't be condemned. Forgive, and you'll be forgiven. Give, and there'll be gifts for you: a full and generous amount will be poured into your lap, for the standard you use for others will be the one that God uses for you.

'Be careful who you follow! You know that one blind man can't lead another; if he does, they'll both fall into a ditch. And be careful who you listen to: pupils aren't greater than their teachers, but at the end of their training all pupils are equal to their teachers.

'Why do you notice the splinter in your friend's eye and not notice the plank in your own? How can you say to your friend, "Let me remove your splinter," when you can't see the plank in your own? You hypocrite! First take the plank out of your own eye, and then you'll see how to take the splinter out of your friend's eye.

'You all know that trees can be recognised by their fruit. Nobody picks figs from thorn bushes, or grapes from brambles. And even a child knows that healthy trees don't produce diseased fruit and rotten trees don't produce good fruit. It's the same with people: good people lift goodness from the good things inside them, and bad people lift badness from the store of badness inside them: the words which flow from a person's mouth come from whatever is in that person's mind.

'Why do some of you call me, "Sir, Sir," and not do what I say? People who come to me and listen to me and obey me, are like a man who digs deep when he builds his house and lays the foundations on solid rock. When the river floods it hits the house, but can't shake it because it's so well built.

'But people who listen to me and do nothing about it are like that man who built his house on soil without any foundations. Do you remember him? His house collapsed as soon as the Jordan flooded – and what a ruin it became.'

Jesus in Capernaum

Jesus returned to Capernaum when he'd finished travelling through Galilee. A Roman officer there had a favourite servant who was sick and dying. When he heard that Jesus had returned, he sent some of the Jewish leaders to ask Jesus to heal his servant.

They pleaded earnestly with Jesus: 'He really deserves your help because he loves our people and paid for our synagogue to be built.'

So Jesus went with them, and when he was near the house the officer sent some friends to say, 'Sir, don't put yourself to any trouble because I don't deserve the honour of receiving you into my house, and I'm not worthy to meet you in person. Just give the order from where you are and my servant will be cured.

'I recognise your authority, for I'm under the authority of superior officers myself, and have soldiers under me: why, I order this one, "Go", and he goes, that one, "Come", and he comes, and my servant, "Do this", and he does it.'

This surprised Jesus, and he turned to the crowd following him and said, 'I tell you that I've never found faith like this before, not in Palaestina.'

And when the officer's friends went back to his house they found his servant in perfect health.

Jesus in Nain

Soon afterwards Jesus went to Nain, accompanied by his disciples and a large number of people. Just as he arrived at the town gate, a funeral procession came out. The dead man was the only son of a widow, and a large crowd of townspeople were with her.

Jesus felt very sorry for her, and said to her, 'Don't cry.' Then he touched the open coffin and the men carrying it stood still.

Jesus said, 'Young man! I tell you to get up.' The dead man sat up and started to talk, and Jesus gave him back to his mother.

The people were frightened, but they praised God saying, 'A great prophet has appeared among us. God has come to save his people.' This news about Jesus spread all over the province.

Jesus and John

When John's followers visited him in prison and told him the news from Nain, he sent two of them to ask Jesus, 'Are you really the one that I said was going to come, or should we expect someone else?'

They reached Jesus and asked him the question. At that very moment Jesus was curing people of diseases, ailments and devils, and was giving sight to some who were blind.

When he'd finished, he answered John's messengers, 'Go and tell John what you've just seen: the blind see, the lame walk, lepers are cured, deaf people hear, dead people live, and good news is proclaimed to the poor. And give him this message from me, "How fortunate are those who have no doubts about me!" '

After the messengers had gone, Jesus talked to the crowds about John. 'What did you expect to see when you went out to the desert? A blade of grass swaying in the breeze? Of course not! What did you go to see? A man dressed in expensive clothes? People who dress like that live in luxury in palaces.

'So what did you go to see? A prophet? Of course! But more than a prophet. I tell you, John's the one that Scripture describes when it says, "Look, I will send my messenger ahead of you to prepare the way for you." I tell you that John is greater than any man who's ever lived – but even the least in God's kingdom is greater than he.'

The people listening to Jesus, including some tax collectors, were the very ones who'd been baptised by John and had acknowledged God's demand that they change their thinking. But the Pharisees and the experts in the Jewish law had rejected God's plan for their lives by refusing to be baptised by John.

Jesus continued talking about John. 'What comparison can I find for the people of this generation? What are they like? They're like the children who sit in the market and shout at each other, "We played wedding music but you wouldn't dance. We sang funeral songs and you wouldn't cry!"

'John came, not eating bread or drinking wine, and you

said, "He's got a devil in him." The Son has come, eating and drinking, and you say, "Look at him. He's nothing but a glutton and a drunkard who's friendly with tax collectors and sinners." Yet God's wisdom is shown to be true by the people who accept it.'

Jesus and Simon

A certain Pharisee invited Jesus to a meal. When he arrived at the house he lay down to eat, but the meal was interrupted by a woman with a bad reputation in the town. She had heard that Jesus was dining with the Pharisee and had brought him an alabaster jar full of ointment.

She stood at Jesus' feet crying. Her tears fell on his feet and she wiped them away with her hair. Then she covered his feet with kisses and poured the ointment over them.

When the Pharisee saw this, he thought, 'If this man really was a prophet, he'd know what sort of woman was touching him.' At that, Jesus sat up and said, 'Simon, I've something to say to you.

'Two men owed money to a banker. One owed him £500, the other owed £50. As neither could pay, the banker let them both off. Which one loved him the most?'

Simon answered, 'I suppose the one who was forgiven the most.'

'You're right,' Jesus said. Then he turned to the woman while he carried on speaking to Simon.

'See this woman? When I entered your home you gave me no water for my feet, but she washed them with her tears and dried them with her hair. You didn't welcome me with a kiss, but she's been covering my feet with kisses ever since she came in. You didn't provide any olive oil for my head, but she's poured all her ointment on to my feet. I tell you, Simon, the great love she shows proves that her sins – even though they're many – have been forgiven. It's only someone who's been forgiven little who shows such little love!'

Then Jesus said to the woman, 'Your sins are forgiven!' Immediately everybody else at the table started muttering to each other, 'Who does he think he is? What man forgives sins?'

But Jesus said to the woman, 'Your faith has saved you. Go in peace.'

After the meal, Jesus travelled again through the towns and villages of Galilee, speaking good news about God's kingdom. The Twelve went with him, as did some women who'd been cured of evil spirits and diseases.

There was Mary (called Magdalene) from whom seven devils had gone out, Joanna (the wife of Herod's steward Chuza), Susanna, and many others who used their own money to help Jesus and his disciples.

(Theo, please place here another extract from John Mark's manuscript. The section from the third star in the margin to the fourth describes Jesus' miracles in Galilee better than my notes.

I can't understand how John Mark found out about so many miracles. He must have got his information from one of the Twelve.)

JESUS' TEACHINGS ON HIS JOURNEYS TO JERUSALEM

As the time approached for Jesus to return to heaven, he determined to go to Jerusalem. He sent messengers ahead, and they went into a village in Samaria to get everything ready for him.

But the people would not receive him because he was going to Jerusalem. When two disciples called James and John saw this, they said, 'Sir, do you want us to call down fire from heaven to burn them?' But Jesus rebuked the two of them, and they went to a different village.

As they travelled along they met a man who said to Jesus, 'I'll follow you everywhere you go.' Jesus answered him, 'Foxes have holes and birds have nests, but I've nowhere to lie down and rest.'

Jesus told another man, 'Follow me!' However, the man replied, 'Sir, please let me go and bury my father first.' Jesus answered hm, 'Leave the dead to bury themselves. It's your duty to go and spread the news of God's kingdom.'

And another man promised, 'I'll follow you, Sir, but first let me say goodbye to my family.' Jesus told him, 'Anyone who starts to plough and then looks back isn't fit for God's kingdom.'

Jesus and his seventy-two disciples

Jesus then picked seventy-two disciples and sent them ahead of him in pairs to all the towns and villages he planned to visit. He told them, 'There's a large harvest ready but only a few workers to gather it in, so ask the owner of the harvest to send workers to do the harvesting.

'You start off now; but remember, I'm sending you like lambs among wolves. So don't take a purse, or a bag, or a spare pair of sandals. Don't stop to greet anyone on the road. And whenever you enter a house, first say, "Peace to this house."

'If a man of peace lives there, your greeting will be effective. If not, it will strengthen you. Stay in one house, accepting whatever food or drink you're offered, for workers should be paid: don't go from house to house begging.

'When you're made welcome in a town, eat what is put before you, cure the sick, and tell the people that God's kingdom is near. But when you're not welcomed in a town, go out into the streets and tell the people that you're wiping their dust off your feet – but remember to warn them that God's kingdom is near. I tell you, on the day they meet God, he'll show more mercy to Sodom than that town!

'How terrible it will be for you, Chorazin! How terrible for you, too, Bethsaida! If the miracles worked in you had been worked in Tyre and Sidon, the people there would have been sitting in sackcloth and ashes long ago to show that they'd changed their minds about sinning. God will be more merciful to Tyre and Sidon than to you, the people of Chorazin and Bethsaida.

'And as for you, Capernaum. Did you want to be raised to heaven? You will be flung down to hell!

'Anyone who listens to you listens to me. Anyone who rejects you rejects me. And those who reject me reject the One who sent me.'

When the seventy-two disciples returned to Jesus they were full of great joy. They said, 'Sir, even devils submit to us when we use your name!'

Jesus told them, 'I watched the devil falling like lightning from heaven. Listen! I've given you authority to tread on snakes and scorpions, and on the whole strength of the enemy. Nothing will ever hurt you. But don't be glad that devils submit to you, be glad that your names are written in heaven.'

At that moment the spirit filled Jesus with great joy, and he said, 'Father, God of heaven and earth, thank you for showing these children what you've hidden from educated men. Yes, Father, that's exactly what you wanted to happen!

'My Father has given me everything. No one knows who the Son is except the Father, and no one knows who the Father is except the Son – and those to whom the Son chooses to reveal him.'

Then Jesus turned to his disciples and spoke to them privately. 'How fortunate you are to see what you've seen! I tell you that many prophets and kings longed to see what you are seeing, but couldn't, and to hear what you are hearing, but didn't.'

Jesus and a lawyer

An expert in the Jewish law came up and tried to test Jesus. 'Teacher,' he asked, 'What must I do to receive eternal life?'

Jesus answered him, 'What's written in the law? How do you understand it?'

The man replied, 'Love God with all your heart, soul, strength and mind; and love your neighbour as you love yourself.'

'That's right!' Jesus said, 'Do this and life is yours.'

But the lawyer wanted to justify his question, and asked Jesus another, 'Who is my neighbour?'

Jesus replied, 'A man was travelling from Jerusalem to Jericho when he was attacked by bandits. They stripped him, beat him, and made off, leaving him half dead.

'It so happened that a priest was travelling on the same road, but when he saw the man he walked by on the other side. In the same way, a Temple assistant came along and saw him: he walked over and peered at the man, but then walked by on the other side.

'However a Samaritan traveller who came by was filled with compassion when he saw him. He poured oil and wine on his wounds and bandaged them up. Then he lifted him on his animal and took him to an inn, where he looked after him. Next day, he gave the innkeeper some money and told him to take care of the man, promising to pay any extra charge on his way back.'

Jesus ended his story by asking the lawyer, 'In your opinion, which of the three was a neighbour to the man attacked by the bandits?'

He answered, 'The one who was kind to him.' And Jesus said, 'Go and behave like the Samaritan yourself!'

Jesus and two women

In the course of their journey they came to a village, and a woman called Martha welcomed Jesus into her house. She had a sister called Mary who sat herself down at Jesus' feet and started listening to his teaching.

Martha was upset that she had to do all the work, and went up to Jesus and interrupted him, saying, 'Sir, don't you care that my sister is leaving me to do all the work by myself? Please tell her to help me.'

But Jesus replied, 'Martha, Martha! You worry and fret about so many things, but few things matter. In fact only one thing really matters. Mary has chosen to do the better thing, and it's not to be taken away from her.'

Jesus' teachings about prayer

One day on the journey Jesus was praying. When he'd finished, a disciple said, 'Sir, please teach us to pray, just as John taught his followers.'

Jesus told them, 'Say this when you pray:

"Father, may your name be respected;
may your kingdom come;
give us each day the food that we need;
forgive us our sins
because we forgive everyone who's indebted to us.
And please do not lead us into a time of testing." '

Jesus then said to his disciples, 'Suppose one of you goes to a friend's house at midnight, and says, "Friend, please lend me three loaves because a friend on a journey has just arrived at my house and I haven't any food to give him."

'Suppose that the man calls out from inside the house, "Don't bother me now. The door's locked shut and my children are in bed. I can't get up to give it to you." I tell you, if the man won't give the bread because of your friendship, he'll have to get up and give it because of your persistence.

'So I say to you, keep on asking God and it will be given to you; go on seeking, and you will find it; keep on knocking, and the door will be opened. For everyone receives when they carry on asking, everyone finds when they continue to search, and the door is always opened for people who go on knocking.

'Would any of you fathers give your son a snake if he asked for a fish? Or a scorpion if he asked for an egg? Of course not! Bad as you are, you know how to give good things to your children! So how much more will the heavenly Father give the spirit to those who ask him!'

Jesus' teachings about devils

Jesus was driving out a devil from a dumb man, and when the devil had gone, the man could speak. This amazed the crowds, but a few people said that Beelzebul, the chief devil, had given him the power to drive out devils.

Some other people tested him by asking him to work a miracle to show that God approved of what he was doing.

Jesus knew what they were all thinking, and said to them, 'Any kingdom which divides against itself is heading for ruin, and a divided family soon falls apart. It's the same with the devil: if his kingdom is divided, how will it last?

'You claim that I drive out devils with Beelzebul's help; if that's so, how do your own people drive devils out? They prove you're wrong. No! I drive out devils with God's power, and this proves that God's kingdom has come without you noticing.

'When a strong man guards his house, his belongings are safe. But when someone stronger than himself attacks and defeats him, the stronger man takes away his weapons and shares out his belongings. So anyone who's not with me is really against me, and the people who won't work with me are working against me.

'When a devil leaves a person it wanders through a dry country looking for somewhere to rest. If it can't find anywhere it says to itself, "I'll return to the home that I came from."

'But when it arrives and finds everything swept and tidied, it goes off and brings seven other devils which are worse than itself. They set up home, and the person is worse off than at the beginning.'

Jesus' teachings to the crowds

Just as he was speaking, a woman in the crowd called out, 'How fortunate is the womb which gave birth to you. And how lucky are the breasts that fed you!'

But Jesus called back, 'Even more fortunate are those who hear God's word and obey it!'

The crowds grew even bigger as they went along, and Jesus said this to them. 'How evil are the people of today! They keep on asking for a miracle, but the only one they'll be given is the miracle of prophet Jonah. Just as Jonah was a sign for the people of Nineveh, so the Son will be a sign to the people of today.

'On the last day, the Queen of Sheba will condemn this generation because she came such a long way to listen to King Solomon's teaching – and I tell you that there's something here which is greater than Solomon.

'On the last day the people of Nineveh will condemn this generation because they changed their minds about sinning when prophet Jonah spoke to them – and I tell you there's something here which is greater than Jonah.

'No one lights a lamp and then hides it away, they put it on a lamp-stand so that people can see the light when they come into the room. I tell you that the lamp of your body is your mind's eye, and when your mind's eye is healthy your whole body is full of light.

'But when your mind's eye is diseased your body is in darkness. So make sure that the light in you isn't dim. If your body is full of light, with no darkness anywhere, it will be bright everywhere, as when a lamp shines brightly on you.'

Jesus and the Pharisees

Jesus had just finished speaking when a Pharisee invited him to dine at his house. Jesus went in and immediately lay down at the table.

The Pharisee expressed surprise that Jesus had not washed before the meal, so Jesus said to him, 'You Pharisees! You clean the outside of your cups and plates, but on the inside you're full of violence and evil. You fools! Didn't God make the inside as well as the outside? If you gave what's on your plates to the poor you'd be properly clean!

'It will be terrible for you Pharisees, because you give God a tenth of your garden herbs but neglect justice and the love that God has for poor people. You should have done these, as well as the other.

'It will be terrible for you Pharisees, because you like to sit in the prominent seats in the synagogue and to be greeted respectfully in public. How terrible for you, because you're like unmarked graves which people walk on without noticing and so become unclean!'

Jesus and the lawyers

Jesus was interrupted by one of the experts on the law who was present at the meal. 'Sir,' he said, 'you insult us when you speak like this.'

But Jesus replied, 'How terrible for you lawyers, too! You put loads on people that are hard to carry, but you don't lift a finger to help them carry their loads.

'How terrible for you, because you build monuments to

the prophets that your ancestors murdered! By doing this you show that you approve of what they did – they killed the prophets, and you're building their tombs!

'That's why God's wisdom said,"I'll send them prophets and apostles; they'll slaughter some and persecute others, so that this generation will have to answer for every drop of prophets' blood that's been shed since the beginning of time – from Abel's blood to Zechariah's, who died between the altar and Holy Place." Yes, I tell you, the people of today will be punished for all their deaths.

'How terrible for you experts in the law! You've taken the key of the house of knowledge, yet you refuse to go in there yourselves, and you're stopping those from entering who want to.'

When Jesus left that house the lawyers and the Pharisees started to criticise him furiously, and they tried to force him to answer their questions: they wanted to catch him out in something he said.

Jesus's teachings to his disciples

Meanwhile the people had gathered in thousands, so much so that they were stepping on each other. Jesus began to speak to his disciples. 'First of all, guard against the Pharisees' yeast – I mean their hypocrisy – for whatever is covered will be uncovered and whatever is hidden will be revealed. What you say in the dark will be heard in daylight, and what you whisper in secret will be shouted from the rooftops.

'My friends, don't be afraid of those who kill the body but afterwards can't do anything worse. No! I'll tell you whom you should fear; fear the one who, after the killing, can throw you into hell. Believe me, he's the one you should fear.

'Can't you buy five sparrows for two pence? Yet God never forgets one sparrow – why, even the hairs on your head have been counted. So there's no need to be afraid, for you're worth much more than many sparrows.

'I tell you, whoever admits in public that they belong to me will be accepted by the Son in front of God's angels. But whoever rejects me in public will be rejected by the Son in front of the angels.

'Everyone who says one word against the Son can be forgiven, but no one who says evil things about the spirit can ever be forgiven.

'When you're dragged before synagogues, magistrates and authorities, don't worry what to say or how to defend yourselves, because the spirit will teach you what to say at the right moment.'

Jesus' teachings about possessions

A man in the crowd called out, 'Teacher, tell my brother to share the property our father left us.'

But Jesus called back, 'My friend, who gave me the right to judge you or decide what should be yours?'

Then Jesus said to everybody, 'Watch out! Guard against every kind of greed, for life does not consist of possessions, no matter how many you have.'

Then he told them a story. 'There was once a rich man who'd had a good harvest. He thought, "What shall I do? I haven't enough room to store all my crops. I know what I'll do, I'll pull down my barns and build bigger ones, where I can store all my grain and my goods. Then I'll say to myself, you lucky man, you've got everything you need for many years to come. Take life easy. Eat. Drink. Have a good time."

'But God said to the rich man, "You fool! Tonight you'll have to give up your life, so who'll get all the things you've collected for yourself?" '

Jesus ended the story by saying to the crowds, 'This is what happens to people who pile up riches for themselves instead of becoming rich in God's sight.'

Then he said to his disciples, 'That's why I tell you not to worry about life, nor about the food you need or the clothes you wear. Life consists of much more than food, and your body is far more important than your clothes.

'Think about the hooded crows. They don't sow or harvest. They don't have store-houses or barns. Yet God feeds them. You're worth much more than crows! Can any of you live longer by worrying? If you can't manage such a small thing, why worry about the rest?

'Think how the wild flowers grow. They don't work or make clothes. Yet I tell you that not even King Solomon with all his wealth had clothes as lovely as theirs. If that's how God clothes a flower, which is growing wild today and is thrown on the fire tomorrow, how much more will he look after you? You've such little faith!

'So don't be choosy about food and drink. And don't worry! For it's people who don't know God who are concerned with these things. Your Father knows that you need food and clothes, so instead be choosy about his kingdom – and all these other things will be given to you as well.

'And there's no need to be afraid about any of this, my little flock of crows, for it's pleased your Father to give you his kingdom!

'So sell your possessions and give to the poor. Get yourselves purses that never wear out, and put your savings in heaven – where no thief can steal and no moth can destroy. Your heart will always be where your riches are!'

Jesus' teachings about the future

Jesus carried on saying to his disciples, 'Always be ready for whatever comes, dressed for quick action with your lamps lit. Be like servants waiting for their master to return from a wedding feast, ready to open the door the moment he knocks.

'How fortunate are those servants whose master finds them

awake when he comes! In truth, I tell you that he'll put on his overalls, sit them down at the table, and then serve them himself.

'How fortunate they are if he finds them ready, especially if he arrives home much later than expected! You can be sure that if the owner of a house knew when a burglar was coming, he wouldn't let him break in. You too must be ready, for the Son will come when you least expect him!'

A disciple called Peter spoke up. 'Sir,' he said, 'is this for us or for everyone?'

Jesus replied, 'Who is the wise and reliable servant that the master will put in charge of his household to ensure that the other servants are properly fed at all the right times?

'How fortunate that servant will be if his master finds him doing that when he returns! Indeed, I tell you the master will put that servant in charge of all his property.

'But if the servant thinks that his master is taking a long time coming, and begins to hit the other servants, and eats and drinks and gets drunk, his master will return unexpectedly and throw him out to the fate of the unreliable.

'The servant who knows what his master wants, but hasn't got ready or done what his master wants, will be severely flogged. But the servant who doesn't know what his master wants, and then does something which deserves a flogging, will only be given a light punishment.

'Much is demanded from the person to whom much has been given, and even more is demanded from the person to whom much has been carefully entrusted.

'I've come to set the earth on fire, and how I wish it was already ablaze! There's one more baptism that I've still to receive, and what distress I feel until it's completed! Do you suppose that I'm here to bring peace to the earth? No! Not peace! Division!

'From now on a family of five will be divided, three against two and two against three. Father against son and son against father. Mother against daughter and daughter against mother. Mother-in-law against daughter-in-law and daughter-in-law against mother-in-law.'

Jesus said to the crowds, 'When you see a cloud coming from the west you say, "That rain's coming," and it is. When the wind blows from the south, you say, "It's going to be hot," and it is.

'You hypocrites! You know what the signs in the sky mean, so why don't you know what the signs of these times mean? Why don't you judge for yourselves what's the right thing to do?

'If someone takes you to court, do your best to settle out of court. If you don't, you may be thrown into prison. I tell you, you won't get out until you've paid the last penny of your fine.'

At about this time some people arrived and told Jesus about the Galileans whom Pilate had killed when they were making their sacrifices. Jesus said to them, 'Because these Galileans were killed in this way, do you think it makes them worse sinners than anybody else? They weren't! But I tell you that if you don't change your minds about sinning you'll die as they did.

'What about those eighteen people in Siloam who died when the tower collapsed? Were they worse than the other people in Jerusalem? Of course not! But unless you change your thinking you'll die as they did.'

Then Jesus told them this story. 'A man planted a fig tree in his vineyard. He went looking for figs but couldn't find any. So he said to his gardener, "I've been waiting for fruit for three years now and there hasn't been any. Chop it down, why should it take up the space?"

' "Sir," the gardener replied, "leave it alone for one more year, and I'll dig round it and put on some manure. That way it may fruit next year. But if not, then you can have it chopped down." '

Jesus and a woman

One Sabbath Jesus was teaching in a synagogue. A woman who was present had a devil which had made her ill for eighteen years. She was bent over and unable to hold her head up erect.

When Jesus saw her, he called out, 'Woman, you're freed from your illness,' and he placed his hands on her. At once she straightened up and praised God.

The synagogue president was angry because Jesus had healed on the Sabbath, and he spoke to the people, 'There are six days for work, so come on one of those days to be healed – not on the Sabbath.'

But Jesus answered him back, 'You hypocrite! Is there anyone here who wouldn't untie his ox or his donkey and take it to water on the Sabbath? And this woman, one of Abraham's daughters whom the devil has kept bound for eighteen years, wasn't it right to untie her on the Sabbath?'

When Jesus said this all his enemies were ashamed of themselves, but the people were overjoyed at the miracles he worked.

Jesus went on to say, 'What's God's kingdom like? What shall I compare it with? It's like this: a man sows a mustard seed in his garden. It grows and becomes a tree, and birds shelter in its branches.'

He asked the same question again. 'What shall I compare God's kingdom to this time? It's like the yeast a woman mixes with forty litres of flour: the whole batch of dough rises.'

Jesus' teachings about the future

Jesus went through towns and villages, teaching the people and making his way to Jerusalem. Someone asked him, 'Sir, will only a few people be saved?'

Jesus replied, 'Try your hardest to enter by the narrow

door, because many people who try to enter won't succeed.

'Once the master of the house has locked the door, you might find yourself standing outside in the cold, knocking and asking for the door to be opened.

'He'll say, "I don't know where you've come from." And then you'll start saying, "But we once ate and drank with you when you taught in our town." However, he'll reply, "I don't know where you come from. Get away from me, you wicked people."

'Then you'll cry and grind your teeth when you see Abraham, Isaac and Jacob, and all the prophets, in God's kingdom – while you're thrown out. People will come from east and west, and from north and south, to sit and feast in God's kingdom. Understand this, there are those who are last now, who'll be first; and there are those who are first now, who will be last.'

Just at this time some Pharisees came up to Jesus and said to him, 'You must get away from this place because Herod is planning to kill you.'

But Jesus replied, 'Go and give that fox this message, "I'll be driving out devils and healing people today and tomorrow, but on the third day I'll finish my work."

'I must carry on with my journey now, and tomorrow, and the next day too, for it wouldn't be right for a prophet to be killed anywhere except Jerusalem.

'Jerusalem! Jerusalem! You kill the prophets and you stone the messengers God sends you! How often I've longed to put my arms round your people, like a hen gathers her chicks under her wings; but you've always refused to let me. Watch out! Your Temple will be abandoned. Yes, I promise you that you won't see me until the day comes when you say, "How fortunate is he who comes in the name of the Lord!" '

Jesus at a meal

One Sabbath, Jesus went to dine in the home of a leading

Pharisee. The people at the meal were watching him closely.

In front of him was a man whose body was swollen with dropsy, so Jesus asked the experts in the law and the Pharisees, 'Is it against the law to heal someone on the Sabbath?'

They wouldn't answer, so Jesus went to the man, healed him, and sent him away. Then Jesus asked them, 'If your son or your ox fell into a well, which of you wouldn't hesitate to pull him out on the Sabbath?' They hadn't got an answer for Jesus!

He then told the guests at the meal a story, because he'd noticed how they'd picked all the best seats.

'When someone invites you to a feast, don't sit in the best seat. A more important person than you may have been invited, and the host may ask you to give up your seat to that man. To your embarrassment, you'll have to move to the worst seat.

'No! When you're a guest, always sit in the least important seats so that your host can invite you to move to a better one. Then the other guests will see you being honoured, for everyone who tries to look important will be humbled, and everyone who acts humbly will be made to look important.'

Then Jesus spoke to his host, 'In future, when you have a party, don't invite your friends, family and rich neighbours – in case they repay you by inviting you back.

'No! Whenever you have a party, invite the poor, the crippled, the lame and the blind. That way you'll be fortunate – they can't repay you, but God will repay you when you meet him.'

When one of the other guests overheard this, he said, 'How fortunate are those who'll share a meal with God in his kingdom!'

Jesus answered him with a story. 'A man gave a great feast and invited a large number of people. When the day arrived he sent his servants to tell the guests that they should come because everything was ready. But they started to make excuses.

'The first said, "I've bought some land and must inspect it; please pass on my apologies." Another said, "I've bought five pairs of oxen and am on my way to try them out; please accept my apologies." A third said, "I've just got married and so am unable to come."

'The servant returned to his master and reported what they'd said. The master was furious, and told his servant, "Quick, go to the town's streets and alleys and bring in the poor, the crippled, the blind and the lame."

'Soon the servant said, "Sir, your orders have been carried out, but there's still some room left." So the master ordered his servant, "Go to the country lanes and the fields and urge people to come in so that my house is filled."

'I tell you that not one of those who were invited will taste any part of the feast.'

Jesus' teachings about becoming a disciple

Large crowds of people were now accompanying Jesus on his journey, and he said this to them, 'Whoever comes to me can't be my disciple unless they love me much more than they love their father, their mother, their wife, their husband, their brothers, their sisters, yes, even themselves.

'You can't be my disciple if you don't carry a cross, the sign of your death, and follow after me.

'Indeed, if any of you intended to build a tower, wouldn't you sit down and work out the cost to see if you'd enough money to finish the job? If not, you mightn't be able to finish the tower after laying the foundations. People would laugh at you. They'd say, "Here's someone who started to build and couldn't finish his tower."

'Or what king marching to war wouldn't first sit down and decide whether his ten thousand men could defeat his enemies' twenty thousand men. If he thinks that they can't, surely he'll send messengers asking for peace while the armies are still some way apart.

'In exactly the same way, none of you can be my disciple unless you give up everything you own. Salt's useful. But if it loses its saltiness there's no way of making it salty again: it's no use for anything and people throw it away. Listen to me then, if you've got ears!'

Jesus' teachings about rejoicing

Tax collectors and sinners were always crowding round Jesus to listen to him, and one day the Pharisees and scribes complained, saying, 'This man welcomes sinners and even eats with them.' So Jesus told them this story.

'Suppose one of you had a hundred sheep, and lost one. Wouldn't you leave the ninety-nine in the desert and search for the missing one until you had found it?

'And then, wouldn't you be so pleased to have found it that you'd carry it home on your shoulders? And wouldn't you call your friends and neighbours together, and ask them to rejoice with you because you'd found the sheep that you'd lost?

'It's exactly the same in heaven! I tell you that there's more rejoicing in heaven over one sinner who changes his mind about sinning, than over ninety-nine good people who don't need to change the way that they think.

'Or again, what woman who'd lost a silver coin wouldn't light a lamp, sweep her house, and go on searching until she found it?

'Wouldn't she then call her friends and neighbours together, and tell them to celebrate with her because she'd found the coin that she'd lost?

'It's exactly the same with God's angels! They really rejoice when a sinner changes her mind!'

Then Jesus said, 'A man had two sons. The younger asked his father for the share of the property which would come to him when the man died. So the father divided his property between the two sons.

'A few days later the son sold his part and left home with the money. He went to a far country where he wasted the money on wild living.

'When his money had gone, the country was hit by a severe famine and he began to suffer. So he went to work for a man who sent him to feed pigs. The son was so hungry that he wished he could eat the pigfood, but no one would let him.

'Then he came to his senses and said, "All my father's workers have more than enough to eat, and here am I starving to death. I'll leave this place and return to my father, and say: 'Father, I've sinned against heaven and you; I don't deserve to be called your son any more, please treat me like one of your workers.'"

'So the son left the farm and went back to his father. While he was still a long way from home, his father saw him and was filled with pity. He ran up to the son, threw his arms round him and kissed him.

'Then the son started saying, "Father, I've sinned against heaven and you, and don't deserve to be called your son any more . . ."

'But his father took no notice and said to his servants, "Quick! Bring the best coat and put it on him. Put a ring on his finger and sandals on his feet. Bring our prize calf and kill it. And let's celebrate with a feast – for my son was dead and now he's alive. He was lost and now he's been found." And so the feast began!

'But the elder son was out in the fields. On his way back, as he got near the house, he heard the music and dancing. So he called a servant over and asked him what it was about.

'The servant told him, "Your brother has come home, and your father has killed the prize calf because he's safe and well."

'This made the brother angry, and he refused to join the

feast. So his father came out and begged him to join in, but the son snapped at his father, "All these years I've slaved for you and never once disobeyed an order, yet you've never even given me a goat to celebrate with my friends. But this other son of yours wastes your property on prostitutes and you kill the prize calf for him!"

'The father replied, "My son!! You're always with me, and everything I have is now yours. But we had to celebrate and rejoice because your brother who was dead has returned to life. He was lost and now he's been found." '

Jesus' teachings about money

Jesus also said to his disciples, 'There was once a rich man with a servant who managed his property. The rich man was told that his manager was wasting his money, so he called the man in. "What's this I hear?" he said, "Draw up a complete account of the way you've managed my property, because you're not going to be my manager any more."

'The manager thought, "What am I going to do when I've been dismissed? I'm too weak to dig, and I'm too proud to beg. Aha! I know what I can do to make sure I've some friends who'll welcome me into their homes!"

'So he called in all the people who owed his master money, and asked the first one, "How much do you owe my master?"

' "One hundred barrels of olive oil" the man replied.

'The manager said, "Here! Take your account. Sit down and quickly write fifty."

'He asked another man, "How much do you owe?"

' "A hundred sacks of wheat," the man answered.

' The manager told him, "Here's your account, change it to eighty."

'When the master found out he praised the dishonest manager for being so shrewd – because the people of this dark world are much more shrewd in dealing with each other than the people who belong to the light.'

Jesus went on, 'So I tell you this, use your money —
polluted as it is — to make yourself a friend. That way, when it
runs out, you'll be invited into his eternal home.

'Anyone who's reliable in small details will be reliable in
large ones, and anyone who's dishonest with small things
will be dishonest with great ones.

'If you can't be trusted with money — that polluted thing
— who's going to trust you with genuine riches? And if you
can't be trusted with external wealth, who'll give you the
riches which go inside you?

'No one can be the servant of two different masters. You'll
either hate the first and love the second, or be attached to
one and despise the other. You can't be the servant of both
God and money!'

When the Pharisees heard this they sneered at Jesus,
because they all loved money. So he said to them, 'You're
the very ones who make yourselves look good in people's eyes,
but God knows what you're like on the inside. And the things
that people value highly are worth nothing to God.

'The things you prize — Moses' law and the prophets'
writings — were only in effect until the time of John. Since
then the good news about God's kingdom has been told, and
I tell you that everyone's trying to force their way in.

'But it is easier for heaven and earth to disappear than for
one small stroke to drop out of the law. For instance, any
man who divorces his wife and marries another woman
commits adultery, and the man who marries a divorced
woman also commits adultery.

'Here's another example: there was a rich man who used
to feast extravagantly every day and dress in fine linen which
had been dyed the colour of purple.

'A poor man called Lazarus, who was covered in sores,
always lay at his gate. Lazarus longed to eat the scraps that
fell from the rich man's table, but nobody offered him a thing.
Even dogs came and licked his sores.

'The poor man died, and was carried away by angels to sit beside Abraham at God's feast in heaven. The rich man also died, and he was buried.

'In his torment in the place of the dead, the rich man looked up and saw Abraham far off, with Lazarus next to him. He cried out, "Father Abraham! I'm in agony in these flames, please pity me and send Lazarus to dip his finger in water and cool my tongue."

'Abraham said, "My son, remember that you had all the good things during your life, while Lazarus had all the bad things. Now it's his turn to enjoy himself and your turn to be in pain. And that's not all: there's a deep pit between us so no one can cross from one side to the other."

'The rich man replied, "Father, I beg you, please send Lazarus to my house to warn my five brothers not to come to this place of torment."

'Abraham said, "But they've got Moses and the prophets to warn them, your brothers should listen to them."

'The rich man answered him, "That's not enough, Father Abraham, but if someone went to them from the dead they'd change the way they think about the poor."

'Then Abraham said to him, "If they won't listen to Moses and the prophets, they won't be convinced when someone returns from the dead." '

Jesus' teachings about serving

Jesus said to his disciples, 'Things which make people fall into sin are bound to happen, but how terrible for the person who makes them happen! It would be better for him to be thrown into the sea with a large stone tied to his neck, than for him to cause just one of these little ones to sin. So watch how you behave!

'If your brother does something wrong, rebuke him. And if he changes his mind, forgive him. If he wrongs you seven times a day, and each times comes back and says that he's changed his mind, you must still forgive him.'

The Twelve said to Jesus, 'Make our faith bigger.' But Jesus told them, 'If your faith was the same size as a mustard seed you'd be able to tell this mulberry tree to jump in the sea – and it would!'

'Suppose you had a servant ploughing or looking after the sheep. If he came in from the fields would you tell him to be comfortable and eat his own meal? Of course not! You'd be much more likely to say, "Get my supper ready first, then serve me while I eat. You can eat later."

'Does a servant deserve thanks for obeying orders? Of course not! It's the same with you. When you've done all you've been told to do, say, "We're useless servants, we've only been doing our duty." '

Jesus and ten sick men

On the way to Jerusalem, Jesus was travelling on the borders of Samaria and Galilee. As he entered one village he met ten men who were suffering from a terrible skin disease. They were highly infectious so they stood some distance away and called to Jesus to have pity on them. When Jesus saw them, he told them to go and show themselves to the authorities.

As they were going away they discovered that they'd been healed. When one of them realised this, he turned back, praised God at the top of his voice, threw himself flat at Jesus' feet, and thanked him. The man was a Samaritan.

This made Jesus say, 'Weren't all ten of you healed? Where are the other nine? It seems to me that no one's come back to give thanks to God except this foreigner.' Then Jesus told the man to stand up. 'Go on your way. Your faith has saved you.'

Jesus' teachings about the future

Some Pharisees asked Jesus when God's kingdom would come,

and he gave them this answer. 'God's kingdom can't be seen. No one will ever say, "Here it is!" or "Look, there it is!" because God's kingdom is something inside you.'

Jesus then said to his disciples, 'The time's coming when you'll long to see a day like today, and won't be able to. People will say, "Here he is!" or "Look, there he is!" But don't move. Don't go looking for me. Just as lightning flashes across the sky, so it will be when the Son's great day arrives. But first he must suffer much and be rejected by the people of today.

'As it was in Noah's day, so will it be in the Son's days. People were eating, drinking and marrying right up to the day Noah went into the ark, and the flood destroyed them all.

'It'll be the same as in Lot's day: people were eating and drinking, buying and selling, planting and building, but the day Lot left Sodom they were all destroyed by fire from heaven. It will be exactly the same when the day comes for the Son to be revealed for who he is.

'When that day comes the man on his roof mustn't go into his house to collect his belongings. And the man in the field mustn't return to his house. Remember Lot's wife! Anyone who tries to save his life will lose it, and anyone who loses it will keep it safe.

'I tell you, that on that night when two people are in bed together, one will be taken and the other one left. When two women are grinding corn together, one will be taken and the other one left.' The disciples asked, 'Taken where?' But Jesus said, 'Where vultures gather there's always a dead body!'

Jesus' teachings about prayer

Then Jesus told them a story to encourage the crowds of disciples to go on praying without getting discouraged. 'In a certain town there was a judge who neither feared God nor respected any person. In the same town there was a widow who kept on coming to him, demanding justice against her enemy.

'The judge refused for a long time, but at last he thought, "Even though I don't fear God or respect anyone, I'm going to have to give this widow her rights because she keeps on pestering me. Why! If I don't, she might come and slap my face!" '

And Jesus said, 'Did you notice what the corrupt judge said? Now, don't you think God will see that justice is done for his people if they keep on calling to him night and day for help – even though he seems slow to help them? I promise you, he will see that justice is done for them. And quickly! But will the Son find any faith on the earth when he comes?'

He spoke this story to some people who were convinced of their own goodness and looked down on everyone else. 'Two men went to the Temple to pray. One was a Pharisee and the other was a tax collector.

'The Pharisee stood there and prayed, "I thank you, God, that I'm not greedy, dishonest, or adulterous like everyone else. And I thank you that I'm not like that tax collector over there. Why! I fast twice a week and give you a tenth of my income."

'The tax collector stood some way away and did not even dare to raise his eyes to heaven. Instead he beat his breast and said, "God, have mercy on me, a sinner."

'I tell you,' said Jesus, 'that the tax collector, and not the Pharisee, went home right with God. For everyone who tries to look important will be humbled, and everyone who humbles themselves will be made to be great.'

(Theo, please insert here the section in John Mark's manuscript which comes between the fifth and the sixth stars that I've put in the margin. It describes what happened at the end of Jesus' last journey – when he was near Jericho and when he first entered Jerusalem.

I was so preoccupied with Zacchaeus that I gathered little information in Jericho about this time.

I'm using so much of Mark's work that I must write and ask his permission!

Will you please also add in the information I sent you about the day Zacchaeus became a follower. It doesn't matter where you put it, because I'll revise everything again when I reach Rome.)

JESUS IN JERUSALEM

The feast of Lamb and Unleavened Bread was near. Jesus spent all day, every day, teaching in the Temple. But each evening he went to the hill called the Mount of Olives and spent the night in the open.

The people began gathering in the Temple first thing each morning to listen to him. The chief priest and the experts on the Jewish law were afraid of the people, so they were looking for a way of secretly killing Jesus.

Then the devil entered one of the Twelve called Judas Iscariot. He approached the chief priests and the officers of the Temple guard to discuss with them some way of handing Jesus over.

They were delighted and agreed to pay him to do this. Judas accepted their offer and started looking for a good opportunity to hand Jesus over without the people knowing about it.

The day came during the festival for the lambs to be killed, and Jesus sent off two disciples to make preparations for them to eat the festive meal.

They asked Jesus, 'Where shall we get it ready?' Jesus told them, 'Look, as you enter the city you'll meet a man carrying a water container. Follow him to the house he enters, and say to the owner of that house, "The Teacher says, 'Where is the room for me to eat the feast with some of my disciples?' "

177

'The man will show you a large upstairs room which is furnished with couches. Make the preparations there.'

Jesus' last meal

The two disciples went off, found everything exactly as Jesus had told them, and prepared the festival meal.

When the time came, Jesus took his place at the table and the Twelve reclined with him. He said to them, 'I've been longing to eat this meal with you before I suffer, because I'll never eat it again until it's been given its full meaning in God's kingdom.'

Then, picking up a cup of wine, Jesus gave thanks to God and said, 'Take this and share it among yourselves. From now on I'll not drink wine until God's kingdom comes.'

Next he took a piece of the bread, thanked God for it, broke it, gave it to them, and said, 'This bread is my body, and it's to be given for you. Do this to remember me.'

Jesus did the same with the cup of wine after the meal, and said, 'This cup is God's new binding promise, it's sealed with my blood which has to be poured out for you.

'But look! The one who betrays me is here at the table. The Son will die in the way that God has decided, but how terrible for the man who betrays him!'

Then the Twelve began to ask each other which one of them could do this. An argument also began to break out among them as to who was the most important.

So Jesus told them, 'Pagan kings have power over their people, and call themselves "Friends of the People". It mustn't be like this with you. No! The most important must behave as if they were the youngest, and the leader must behave like a servant.

'Who's the most important: the one who sits down, of course. But here I am as the one who serves!

'You've stayed with me throughout my trials; and just as my Father has given me the right to rule, so I'll give you the same right. You'll eat and drink at my table in God's kingdom, and you'll sit on thrones to rule over the twelve tribes of Palaestina.'

Jesus talks to Peter

Then Jesus spoke to one of the Twelve called Peter. 'Peter! Listen to me. The devil's been given permission to test all of you, to separate good from bad the way farmers separate grain from husks. But I've prayed for you, Peter, that your faith won't fail. When you've recovered, you must strengthen the others.'

Peter replied, 'Sir, I'm ready to go to prison with you and to die with you.'

Jesus said, 'I tell you, Peter, by the time the cock crows tomorrow morning you'll have denied knowing me three times.'

Then Jesus said to them all, 'Did you lack anything when I sent you out without a purse, a bag, or sandals?'

'No! Nothing!' they replied.

He said, 'Well now, if you've got a purse or a bag you must take it. And if you haven't got a sword you must sell your coat and buy one. I tell you that the Scripture which says, "He shared the fate of criminals" is about to come true for me.'

They said to him, 'Sir, we've got two swords here.'

And Jesus told them, 'That's enough!'

Jesus prays

Jesus then left the city and made his way, as usual, to the Mount of Olives, and the disciples followed him. When he reached the place, he said to them, 'Pray that you're not tested.'

Then he went off from them, about a stone's throw away, and knelt down to pray. 'Father,' he prayed, 'if you're willing, please take this cup of suffering away from me. Even so, let your will be done, not mine.'

Then an angel from heaven appeared to give Jesus the strength that he needed. In great anguish Jesus prayed even more fervently, and his sweat fell to the ground like great drops of blood.

When Jesus rose up from his prayers, he went across to the disciples and found them asleep, worn out by their grief. He said to them, 'Why are you asleep? Get up and pray that you're not put to the test.'

Jesus' arrest

Suddenly, while Jesus was speaking, several men arrived, led by Judas Iscariot, one of the Twelve. He went up to Jesus to kiss him, but Jesus said, 'Judas! Are you really going to betray me with a kiss?'

When the disciples with Jesus realised what was happening, they said, 'Sir, shall we use the swords?' And one of them struck the High Priest's servant and chopped off his right ear.

'That's enough!' Jesus said, and he touched the man's ear and healed him.

Then Jesus said to the chief priests, the officers of the Temple guard, and the elders who'd come for him, 'Did you really have to come for me armed with swords and clubs as though I were a bandit? You didn't try to arrest me when I was with you in the Temple day after day. But this is your hour – this is the rule of darkness.'

Jesus and Peter

They arrested Jesus, and took him away to the High Priest's house. Peter followed at a distance. They'd lit a fire in the middle of the courtyard, and Peter joined those who were sitting there.

When a servant girl saw him sitting by the fire, she peered at him, and said, 'This man was with Jesus.' But Peter denied it, saying, 'Woman! I don't even know him.'

A little bit later another man insisted, 'You're one of them.' But Simon Peter replied, 'I'm not, my friend.'

About an hour later another man noticed Peter, and said, 'This man was definitely with him. Why, you can tell by his accent that he's from Galilee.'

Peter answered, 'I don't know what you're talking about.'

At that moment, while he was still speaking, a cock crowed, and Jesus turned round and looked straight at Peter. And Peter remembered the words that Jesus had said, 'Before the cock crows you'll have denied knowing me three times.'

Peter went outside, and wept bitterly. Meanwhile, the men guarding Jesus were mocking and beating him. They blindfolded him and asked him, 'Go on! Guess who hit you!' And they said many other insulting things to him.

Jesus' trial

When day came, the elders, chief priests and lawyers all met together. Jesus was brought before the Jerusalem Council, and they said, 'Tell us if you're the Christ, the Messiah.'

Jesus replied, 'You won't believe me if I do tell you; and you won't answer me if I ask you a question. But from now on I'll be sitting on the right of Almighty God.'

They all called out, 'So you are the Son of God, then?' He answered, 'That's what you say.' Then they said, 'We don't need any witnesses. We've heard it from his own lips.'

The whole group got up and took Jesus to Pontius Pilate, the Roman Governor, where they began to accuse him by saying, 'We caught this man misleading our people, urging them to revolt, telling them not to pay taxes to Rome, and claiming to be the Christ.'

Pilate asked Jesus, 'Are you the king of the Jews?'

'That's what you say,' replied Jesus.

Pilate then told the chief priests and the crowd, 'I find no case against this man.'

But they insisted even more strongly, 'His teaching is starting a riot among the people all the way from Galilee, where he began, all over Judea, even down to here.'

When Pilate heard this he asked if Jesus was a Galilean. As soon as he realised that he was from the region ruled by Herod, who was also in Jerusalem at that time, he passed him over to Herod.

Jesus and Herod

Herod was delighted to meet Jesus because he'd heard about him and had been wanting to see him for a long time. He was especially hoping to see Jesus work a miracle. Herod asked Jesus many questions, but Jesus wouldn't answer them. The chief priests and lawyers were there all the time, vigorously pressing their charges.

Herod and his soldiers treated Jesus with contempt and poked fun at him, then they wrapped him in a prince's cloak and sent him back to Pilate. Herod and Pontius Pilate had been enemies before this, but from that day on they became firm friends.

Jesus and Pilate

Pilate then called together the chief priests, the leaders, and the people. He told them, 'You brought this man before me and said that he was misleading the people. I've personally investigated the matter in front of you and find no grounds for any of the charges you've made. Neither has Herod, for he's sent him back to us. You can see that the man has done nothing to deserve death. So I'm going to have him flogged, and then I'm going to let him go free.'

But the people called out, 'Kill him! Release Barabbas!' (He'd been put in prison for starting a riot and committing a murder.) Pilate wanted to release Jesus, so he spoke to them again. But the crowd yelled back, 'Execute him! Execute him!'

Pilate tried a third time. 'What harm has he done? I can find nothing that deserves the death penalty. I will have him flogged for you, but then I must let him go free.'

The crowd kept on shouting at the tops of their voices, demanding that he be executed, and finally their shouting succeeded. Pilate passed the sentence that they'd been asking for. He set Barabbas free, and he handed Jesus over for them to do as they pleased.

Jesus and some women

As the soldiers led Jesus away, they grabbed a man, Simon from Cyrene, who was coming into the city from the country, and made him carry the cross behind Jesus.

A large crowd of people followed him, and among them were many women who wept and cried for him. But Jesus turned and spoke to them, 'Daughters of Jerusalem! Don't cry for me. Cry instead for yourselves and your children, for the days are coming when people will say, "How lucky are the childless!" Those will be the days when people ask the mountains to fall on them. If those things happen when wood is still green, what'll happen when it's dry?'

Jesus' execution

Two other men, both criminals, were led out with Jesus to be executed. When they reached the place called 'The Skull' they nailed Jesus to a cross, and the two criminals on either side of him.

Jesus said, 'Father, forgive them. They don't know what they're doing.' Then the soldiers played dice to share out his clothing.

The people stood there watching while the Jewish leaders

jeered Jesus. 'He saved others, so let him save himself – if he really is God's Christ, the chosen Messiah.'

The soldiers mocked him as well, coming up and offering him cheap wine, and saying, 'Save yourself if you're the king of the Jews.' Nailed above Jesus was a sign saying, 'This is the king of the Jews!'

Jesus and the criminals

One of the criminals hanging there hurled insults at Jesus. 'Aren't you the Christ? Save yourself and us as well.'

But the other one rebuked him. 'Don't you have any fear of God?' he said. 'You got the same sentence as him, and deserved it, but this man's done nothing wrong.'

Then he said, 'Jesus, please remember me when you come into your kingdom.'

And Jesus answered him, 'In truth I tell you, you'll be with me in paradise today.'

Jesus' death

At noon, the sun's light suddenly vanished and it was dark all over the country until three in the afternoon. Then the curtain in the Temple's holiest place was ripped down the middle.

At that moment, Jesus cried out in a loud voice, 'Father! I place my spirit into your hands.' And with these words, he died.

When a centurion standing nearby saw what had happened he praised God, and said, 'He was a good man.' And when the crowds saw what had happened they went home beating their breasts.

All Jesus' friends stood a short distance away, as did the women who'd come with him from Galilee. They all saw this happen.

Jesus' burial

A member of the Jerusalem Council then arrived, a good man called Joseph who hadn't agreed with what the other members of the Council had done. He came from a town called Arimathaea, and lived in the hope of seeing God's kingdom.

Joseph went to see Pilate and asked for Jesus' body. He took it down, wrapped it in cloth, and placed it in an unused tomb which had been dug out of solid rock. It was Preparation Day, and the Sabbath was about to begin.

The women who'd come with Jesus from Galilee followed behind Joseph: they noted where the tomb was and how the body had been laid. Then they returned and prepared some spices and ointments, before resting on the Sabbath as their law required.

The first day of the week

On the first day of the week, very early in the morning, the women went to the tomb with their spices. They found that the stone had been rolled away from the entrance to the tomb, but when they went in they couldn't find Jesus' dead body. They stood there wondering what had happened when two men in shining clothes suddenly appeared at their side.

The women were terrified and bowed to the ground. But the two men said, 'Why are you looking among the dead for someone who's alive? He's not here, he has returned to life. Don't you remember what he told you in Galilee: "It's been planned that the Son will be handed over to evil men, and be executed, and rise again on the third day"?

Then the women remembered what Jesus had said, and they returned from the tomb and told all this to the Eleven and the other disciples. (The women were Mary of Magdala, Joanna, and Mary the mother of James.) They, and the other women with them, told the Eleven; but they thought it was nonsense and would not believe them.

Peter, however, ran to the tomb to check. He bent down, looked in the tomb, and saw the cloths but nothing else. Then he went back, amazed at what had happened.

Jesus and Cleopas

That same day, two of the disciples were walking to a village called Emmaus, seven miles from Jerusalem. They were discussing what had happened, and as they were talking, Jesus came up and walked by their side. However, they failed to recognise him.

He said to them, 'What are all these things that you're discussing?'

They stopped. Their faces were sad. Then one of them, Cleopas, said, 'You must be the only person in Jerusalem who doesn't know what's been happening in the last few days!'

'What things?' he asked.

'All about Jesus of Nazareth,' they answered, 'who showed everyone that he was a powerful prophet. The chief priests and our own leaders handed him over to be executed. We had hoped that he would set Palaestina free.

'And that's not all. Two days have gone by since this happened, and some women in our group have amazed us. First thing this morning they went to the tomb, and when they couldn't find his body they came back to tell us that they'd had a vision of angels who'd said he was alive!

'Some of our friends have since visited the tomb, and have found everything to be exactly as the women reported. But they saw nothing of him.'

Then Jesus spoke to them, 'You fools! You're so slow to believe the prophets! Wasn't it necessary for the Christ to suffer before he entered his glory?'

Then, starting with Moses and going through the prophets, he explained to them all the Scriptures which dealt with himself.

When they got near to the village he acted as if he were going farther on, but they pressed him to stay with them. 'It's nearly evening,' they said, 'and it's getting dark.' So he went in to stay with them.

He lay down at the table to eat with them, picked up the bread, and said a prayer of thanksgiving. Then he broke the bread and handed it to them. At that moment they realised who he was, but he had vanished from their sight.

They said to each other, 'Wasn't it like fire inside us when he was explaining the Scriptures on the road?'

They instantly got up, left their house, and ran back to Jerusalem, where they found the Eleven gathered with the other disciples – who told them that Jesus had risen, and had appeared to Peter.

Jesus and his disciples

Then they told their story of what had happened on the road, and how they'd recognised Jesus when he broke the bread. They were still talking about this when Jesus himself stood among them and said, 'Peace be with you!'

They were terrified, and thought they were seeing a ghost. But he said, 'Why are you alarmed? What are these doubts in your minds? You can see by my hands and feet that it's me. Go on! Touch me! See for yourselves. Ghosts don't have flesh and bones like me!'

While he said this he showed them his hands and feet, and their joy was so great that they couldn't believe it – they were dumbfounded. So Jesus said to them, 'Have you got anything to eat?' And they offered him a piece of grilled fish – which he ate before their eyes.

Then he told them, 'This is what I meant when I said, when I was still with you, that everything written about me in the Law of Moses, in the Prophets, and in the Psalms, had to come true.'

Then he opened their minds to understand the Scriptures and said, 'So you see, it really is written that the Christ would suffer, and would return from the dead on the third day, and that – in his name – the change of mind to receive the forgiveness of sins would be preached to all nations, beginning in Jerusalem.

'You are witnesses of all this, and now I'm going to send you what the Father has promised. But first you must stay in the city until the power from above comes upon you.'

Jesus returns to heaven

Then Jesus took them out of the city as far as Bethany, where he raised his hands and prayed for them. As he prayed, he left them and was carried up to heaven. They worshipped him and then went back to Jerusalem, filled with great joy. They spent all their time in the Temple giving thanks to God.

I never did find out everything about his disappearance, but I know it took longer than this. I'm not sure whether to alter this report when I rewrite it, or to place the story at the start of my new work.

I hope that you've enjoyed this, the first version of my report, Theo; and that it's made you change your mind about many things.

Best wishes,

Luke.

Timothy Pain
c/o Scripture Union
130 City Road
London
EC1V 2NJ

24th October AD1992

A letter from the editor

Dear Reader,

It was extremely fortunate that Luke used a different boat to send Theo the notes he'd made during his two years in Caesarea Maritima. Because history tells us that the boat which carried Paul, Luke, Aristarchus and Julius sank in a hurricane off the coast of Malta.

The two hundred and seventy-six people on board managed to survive, but the ship was destroyed and they lost their cargo of grain and all their possessions – including Quartus' manuscript.

Of course, I'm sure you've realised by now that nobody found a packet of old letters in an ancient Greek urn! I do have twin boys, but I've never been to Greece!

In this book I've mixed fact and fiction to describe what could have happened back in those amazing days when Luke was researching his gospel in Palestine.

I've relied on the information which Luke gives in the second report he sent Theo (it's usually called 'Acts'), on other historical accounts of that period, and on the revised edition of this report (it's usually called 'Luke').

For instance, in 'Acts', Luke writes about the horse he rode, he gives details of Paul's imprisonment in Caesarea Maritima, introduces Philip and his four prophetic daughters, and implies that Paul didn't like travelling by boat.

I obtained details like the riots in Maritima and the

assassination of Jonathan from other reliable records. And many scholars think that Luke must have discovered most of the facts I've described him finding, in something like the manner I've suggested.

Many of the characters I've introduced are found in 'Luke' or 'Acts' – like Mnason, Joanna, Aristarchus, Manaen, Mary, Cleopas, Philip, Simon, James, Lysias, Lydia, Julius, Festus, Felix, Timothy and Zacchaeus; though many of my characters are fictitious – like Julia, Dedan, Gedor, Hakkoz, Eleazar, Lebanah, Tiras, Flavius and Shavsha.

Most scholars think that Luke used Mark's manuscript in something like the way I've suggested, and that he also used another manuscript which they usually call 'Q'. Nobody knows who wrote it, or what happened to it, and the 'Q' stands for the German word 'Quelle', which means 'source', rather than for 'Quartus'!

Most of the locations in this book are intelligent guesses: there's bound to be some that are bulls-eyes, some that are near-misses, and some that are wildly inaccurate!

Because we know that Luke did lose everything in the Maltese shipwreck, and because we do have his report today, we know that he must have sent his carefully researched notes to someone – and it seems to me that Theophilus is the most likely candidate!

We also know what happened to many of the people who appear in this book. Porcius Festus was a sick man who died in Maritima in AD62, only two years after taking office. The High Priest took advantage of the vacuum created by Festus' unexpected death to kill James by stoning him before the next Governor arrived: Cleopas' son then became the leader of the Way in Jerusalem.

Paul and Luke eventually reached Rome, and Paul was held under house arrest for two more years until he was released in AD63. Paul wrote several of the letters found in the New Testament during those years. We don't know where he went next, but it seems that he was rearrested and executed in Rome in AD67.

Rome burnt to the ground in July AD64, and this was followed by the massive persecution of Christians which the Emperor Nero introduced – before committing suicide in June AD68.

In the summer of AD66, severe rioting broke out again in Caesarea Maritima. This time it led to an uprising against the Romans in Galilee, and to a civil war which was fought throughout Palestine from the winter of AD66 until September AD70, when the Romans finally destroyed Jerusalem. Most of the people in this book – or their real-life equivalents – would have died in the dreadful massacres which took place during those four bloody years.

Nobody knows what happened to Luke. He probably revised this report while caring for Paul in Rome, as well as writing his history of the Way which runs from Jesus' ascension in AD33 until Paul's imprisonment in Rome in AD61–3.

I'm sure he'd have called it nonsense if anyone had suggested to him that he'd become the best selling author in human history. But that's what happened, for he contributed more words to the New Testament than anyone else – even more than Paul.

I think it's wonderful to know that one day I'll meet Luke, and that I'll be able to ask him what really happened – though I expect there'll be a very long queue to talk to him.

If you want to read the revised report which Luke sent Theophilus (and his second report as well) you can find them towards the back of any Bible. But make sure that you borrow or buy a modern translation like the New Jerusalem Bible, the New International Version, or the Good News Bible.

I hope that you've enjoyed this book. Now please pass it on to someone else, or – better still – buy them their own copy!

With best wishes,